DOES SEX

HAVE AN

EXPIRATION

DATE?

DOES SEX

HAVE AN

EXPIRATION

DATE?

Rethinking Low Libido for Women

(aged 35-105)

& the Men Who Love Them

A Guide to Developing Your

Ageless Sex Life

Susana Mayer, PhD

Rhapsody Hill Books, Philadelphia, PA

Cover design by AlphaVision Studio

Author photo by Chingi Zdyrko

This book is not a substitute for professional medical advice, diagnosis, or treatment. Always seek the advice of your physician or other qualified health provider with any questions you may have regarding a medical condition. Never disregard professional medical advice or delay in seeking it.

Published in the United States of America by Rhapsody Hill Books, an imprint of West Philly Press LLC

Westphillypress.com/Rhapsody/

ISBN 978-1733994811

DEDICATION

There would probably be no book if it were not for Dr. Frances Seidman, my chosen mom. She was a "gift" from my biological mother, who insisted we meet in the late 1990s. Frances invited me into her home and into her life in 2002, soon after my mother died unexpectedly and shortly after her husband of 64 years passed away.

Frances gave me the opportunity and courage to persevere through my dissertation and this book. She taught me through her actions that sexuality and sensuality can transcend all expectations and challenges of aging. She still flirted and hugged with a woman's delight from her death bed, shortly before her last breath in 2017 at $100\frac{1}{2}$. She loved men, she loved women, she loved life itself. My only regret is that she is not here to witness and read the final product, in which she encouraged me.

Frances, wherever you are, this book is for you.

Between stimulus and response there is a space. In that space is our power to choose our response. In our response lies our growth and our freedom.

Attributed to Viktor Frankl

CONTENTS

GETTING STARTED

I believe we have the ability to choose our catalysts for change. This book can serve as a prompt to influence parts of your life that have been intentionally ignored or left lying dormant.

But this book needs more than your scrutiny, it needs your words: a few questionnaires to be filled out and passages marked for future contemplation and perhaps to share with your partner. I suggest you create a private, comfortable space, where you feel at ease and have the time to devote to "you." Keep a pen handy, because this book is waiting for your highlights and your notes in the margins. Indeed, the book's margins were explicitly kept wide to ensure you have room for your thoughts prompted by reading—and reflecting on the text. Of course, if your thoughts need more space, have paper close by where you can add to your commentary. I suggest placing the book's page number next to any comments on your extra sheet.

Throughout this text, you will notice sections where you are directed to the book's website for more information. I have intentionally left out such reference-related website links from the text itself, because there is no way to connect to these sites within a paper book format. Plus, I find it personally frustrating when I am given a URL that is no longer valid. At the book's website, URLs will be kept up to date.

This book was designed as a work in progress, since the subject is constantly being studied. New research often produces new insights, theories and sometimes medical advances to help you deal with the challenges of menopause. It is my sincere hope that you visit the book's website often, to keep up to date with these additions and revisions.

Book Website: http://susanamayer.com/book-resources/

DISCLAIMER

This book is not intended as a substitute for medical advice. It is best to consult your physician or qualified healthcare practitioner to make certain that your symptoms do not require medical attention.

PREFACE

Life circumstances had me back at school in my 50s, finishing undergraduate studies and gaining a PhD in Human Sexuality at age 61. As if the rigors of graduate school weren't enough, hot flashes and a fading memory followed me throughout the entire academic process. However, the advantage of being an older student became apparent while studying and researching sexuality in the context of aging and menopause.

When I was conducting interviews with older women collecting data for my undergraduate thesis and doctoral dissertation research, many of them admitted that they would have been hesitant in divulging their intimate details to a much younger person. (They clearly understood that I was a fellow traveler, and on more than one occasion we even found ourselves fanning in sync, all in hopes of that "personal sauna" passing quickly.) My research benefited greatly from the richness of their in-depth disclosures, plus the questions they raised after the official interview process ended. I realized most of the answers to their concerns could probably be supplied by an adult sex-education course—but none existed.

This book evolved out of their questions and the information gathered during these interviews. I decided to focus on menopausal* women's lack of desire for sex, since this topic was of most concern to these women, especially how it had been affecting their relationships. They often referred to their lack of desire as their "low *libido*.*" Simply stated, libido is the physical and psychic energy to create the desire for sex. How the libido functions, however, is far more complicated and will be addressed throughout the text. (Words followed by an asterisk [*] throughout the text are defined in the Glossary in the back of the book.)

Shortly after receiving my doctorate, I found myself in a plight similar to that of some of the women I had interviewed. Surrounded by a massive bookcase filled with self-help books and academic texts on sexuality, I realized one day my own sexual spark was gone. I was in the midst of researching various sexual response cycles when I noticed I no longer thought about having sex myself. With virtually no more spontaneous sexual thoughts and fantasies, my desire for desire had almost vanished. The irony of the situation didn't elude me—I laughed until I cried, tears of self-pity streaming down my cheeks. I was missing the internal sensations that had always jumpstarted my fantasies or converted directly into my desire for sex, and had me waiting impatiently for my lover while lounging in slinky lingerie. As I recalled the interviewees' challenges with sexuality and realized that I was on a similar sexual path, "sexual desire*" was beginning to feel rather elusive. And I missed sharing my sexual spark with my lover. He missed it in me as well.

I decided I wanted to revive my desire for sex. So I revisited the research material I had collected during the interviews. Instead of merely re-evaluating the data, this time I focused on the practical suggestions some of the women had shared with me.

After consulting with a gynecologist and studying further some of the research respondents' recommendations, I modified what they suggested to suit my own circumstances and discovered my new *Personal Path to Pleasure*. It worked! My interest in having sex was renewed, and I was smiling again, as was my lover. And, as so often happens when individuals find a remedy for their ills, I wanted to shout it from the mountaintops and share it with fellow sufferers and their partners. I began to talk with women about what I had learned, and they encouraged me to write this book.

My title of "sexologist" seems to open the floodgates for confessions and questions regarding sexual desire and physical responses. Most women want to understand the changes they are experiencing as they age, plus recommendations about how best to manage them. Some women want to rekindle their sexual spark. Other women who have lost interest in creating the desire for desire are trying to figure out how to keep their husbands' eyes from wandering. Men are also highly interested in my answers to their questions, especially if in their households sex feels like a forbidden subject not open for discussion.

As I compiled the background material and began the writing, I recognized just how much my own circumstances contributed to the project. The suggestions and exercises that follow deal not only with typical menopausal symptoms, but also incorporate my own struggles with physical challenges and pain. This adds a layer of personal experience to the content, which is fundamentally informed by my professional training.

This book offers a wealth of diverse information because I believe in offering a variety of choices, giving people the opportunity to determine what options fit their needs best. I have also included background about the various human sexual response cycles to give you the opportunity to understand how the "low libido" label can be incorrect or misleading. Moreover, you will be introduced to my own version of the human sexual response cycle, the *Sexual Pleasure Model**.

My guidelines and recommendations, along with evaluations of various products and treatments, are presented through the bi-focal lens of my being both sexologist and patient. I have integrated the divergent and often times colliding views from health care professionals to offer additional perspectives on the issues raised by the women who inspired this text. My hope is that you will evaluate the options and make your own informed choices, creating the outcome you desire.

Warning! This book is not politically correct. Having spoken with and gathered research information from heterosexual women, I am addressing their specific needs. However, women in same-sex or gender variant relationships can relate to many of the same issues. Even women traversing through life solo can gain important information regarding their sexuality. For uniformity and ease of reading, the pronoun usage is consistent with heterosexual couples.

The word "older" is used throughout the book; it basically refers to people aging, as we all do, the moment we are born. I have focused on women aged 35 and older, since that is the time some women start to experience the hormonal imbalance of menopause. I have intentionally not used the word "old" because of its pejorative overtones.

The women I interviewed, along with the men who pine for them, influenced the format of this book as well as the content. Both sexes indicated that they often feel inundated with material related to sexual desire, either fluff magazine articles written mainly by well-meaning "sexperts" (there are but a few highly informed ones) or thick texts with too much medical terminology and theory but little practical information. They asked that the book be "not too long" and urged me to "make it easy to understand, but don't dumb it down." I have taken all their suggestions to heart and, hopefully, have presented the material in the manner they requested.

Sharing and Support from Your Partner

I often hear the plea, "please write a book for men, they just don't understand…" and then a succession of issues pour out about relationships, health challenges, and women's experiences. Men also confide in me and express an interest in understanding all the changes that are impacting their wife's sexuality. However, the data have shown most men do not purchase this type of book. I pondered this dilemma for quite some time. Since this book focuses on how menopause affects relationships, I needed to incorporate men in their partner's quest for an *Authentic Sex Life.** So in place of the book men won't read, here is a brief guide on how to personalize the material in this book and introduce it to your partner.

The best approach to customizing the book is to recognize that the more information you share with your partner, the greater potential you have for strengthening your intimate bond. The exercise of sharing gives you the opportunity to present topics you have not discussed previously, or topics you tried to talk about in the past but were met with skepticism. These include sexual secrets you might have guarded because of shame, various physical symptoms, self-esteem issues, and a host of others that are discussed in the book with examples from other menopausal women. If your partner ever doubted your complaints, you now have examples to prove otherwise.

The first step in the process to individualizing this book is to read through it and mark the sections you want to share with your partner. I encourage you to be detailed and to write in the margins specifically what type of support you would like, how you relate to a specific passage (e.g., experience a similar symptom), and any personal information you wish to share with your partner.

After you have completed the markings and filled out the various questionnaires, sit with the book for a while. Decide whether you want to approach your husband one on one, or include a therapist for some or all of the sections you wish to discuss with him.

There might never be "the perfect" opportunity to approach your husband, but there are definitely unsuitable times. If you are uncertain whether he is available emotionally to discuss this topic—ask him. (For example: "I have some important information I would like to share with you, but want to make certain you are not being distracted by other serious issues.")

When you think he is ready, or he has told you so, explain to him that you would like to set up a time to meet and discuss a book you read recently. I have provided a couple examples of hypothetical talks to help you do this.

The first examples refer to finding the time to talk.

Wife: Honey, could we find some time this week to spend at least an hour talking about a book I recently read?

Husband: Oh, you mean the one on your nightstand?

Wife: Yes, that's the one.

Husband: What is there to talk about? We haven't had sex in ages, but if that book has changed your mind, then let's just go to bed.

Wife: We need to speak first—it is far more involved than just having sex.

Husband: Sex is sex.

Wife: That might be the case for you, but not for me. I really want you to have your needs met, and I know that is not happening right now—and I feel bad. Can you just give me an hour to explain?

Husband: Oh sure.

Or:

Wife: Honey could we find some time this week to spend at least an hour talking about a book I recently read?

Husband: Sure—what's it about?

Wife: Well the subject is sex, but specifically low libido, which as you know I'm experiencing.

Husband: Did it give you a remedy?

Wife: Well yes and no, but I'd like to explain in detail, and I would like your input. I know you have been frustrated with my rejections and I want to change that. But it will take at least an hour to explain.

Husband: Well, I've got the time now.

Wife: Okay. (Only if the circumstances feel right.)

Or:

Wife: Now is not a good time for me, but how about...

The following examples are sample introductions to asking for support:

She is sitting on a comfortable couch close by her husband, looking at him the entire time they are speaking, and holding his hands.

Wife: This is really hard for me to talk about, since we haven't had a conversation about sex where one of us hasn't gotten angry and walked away disappointed. I really want to change that, so please be patient with me.

Husband: Well if it is going to get me more sex, sure.

Wife: This book (show him book) has made me realize we both need to get our sexual needs met so we can have a more intimate relationship.

Husband: I'm liking this book already.

Wife: Well, it is not as simple as you might think, and that is the part we need to talk about.

Husband: But sex is simple—you just do it.

Wife: For me it is not, and that is why I am asking for your support in finding what the book calls an *Authentic Sex Life*.

Husband: Never heard of that one.

Wife: Well neither did I until I read the book and learned a lot about sex.

Husband: I thought you knew a lot—you were once really "hot."

Wife: Thanks, I appreciate that compliment. Unfortunately, a lot has changed with my body, and I really need to share that with you. But I haven't.

Husband: Well then tell me.

Wife: I will, but it is rather complicated. (Shows him the book.) I marked up the sections of the book I'd like to go through together. I need to explain the kind of support I would like and find out how you feel about it.

Husband: Wow! That's a lot of markings. How long will this take? Can we do it now? I have another half an hour before my golf game.

Wife: Okay, let's start. I don't know how long it will take, but if we don't finish now, let's set up a time to continue later.

Or:

Wife: I don't know how long it will take, but let's set up a time to meet again with at least an hour to start going through the book.

All of the "wife" dialog in these fictitious scenarios need to be paraphrased so they are in your own voice and applied to your own circumstances.

The directives below will help you establish a *Conscious Coupling.**

- Before you talk to your partner, read through the entire book and mark the passages you want to share.
- Include additional comments in the margin to personalize text.
- Fill out the questionnaires.
- Approach your partner to discuss this book (see previous sample conversations).
- Make certain you have set aside initially at least one hour when you can both focus on each other and not be disturbed by any outside factors. (Phones, kids, etc.)
- Choose a quiet and comfortable space where you can sit close or within reach of each other.

- Position yourself so you can look into each other's eyes when you are speaking. Either sit across from each other, or on a couch, where you will have to position your bodies to comfortably face each other.
- Holding hands can make for a special connection, but only if it feels right.
- While you are going through your markings and words in the margin, talk about why these are important to you.
- Make it clear if you need emotional and/or physical support relating to a specific issue, to help you create an *Authentic Sex Life.*
- Point out sections that you can relate to because you have experienced similar issues, sensations, and/or symptoms.
- When disclosing information never discussed previously, be prepared when your partner asks why you withheld this from him.
- If you have consulted with your physician prior to discussing this book, share any changes in your medical condition that could impact your sexual responses.
- Encourage your partner to see a physician if you think he might have a medical condition that is impacting his sexual expression.
- Encourage your partner to answer some of the questionnaires if you feel it would help you in creating your *Authentic Sex Life.*
- A good place to start when you decide to share this book is the sex quiz below. It is a general quiz that can be used as a jumping off point for discussions or personal sharing.

Some essential points to follow and share with your partner:

- Be present: You might not be available 100% of the time. But when you are together, give 100% of yourself.
- Listen to cues: Any type of physical expression, sounds, and non-verbal signals inform your partner's desires. They are important elements to be considered when pleasuring.
- Ask: When not certain of your partner's preferences or anything to do with the expression of sexuality, don't guess—ask. You are each experts of your own body. If you feel uncomfortable asking, that is another topic to be discussed.
- Do not assume "all women" like the same form of pleasuring or "all men."

- Do not limit your style of pleasuring to your past experiences or what you enjoy. Each person has their individual path to pleasure, and enjoys different touch styles. Also, people's paths change over time.
- Aging and health issues can produce changes in the body, but it is our attitude that affects how we deal with them.

I invite you to join the countless women who have consulted with me, and discover your *Authentic Sex Life*. Taking the quiz below is the first step in this process of discovery.

Mark either *true* or *false* after the statements using the first answer that comes into your head. If you are not certain, make a guess. (The true/false assessment of the statements can be found below the quiz.)

Sex Quiz

1. Sex must be spontaneous to be natural.

2. Women always have to feel sexual desire to want sex.

3. Having sex always has to include orgasm for satisfaction.

4. You can't enjoy sex with your partner if you masturbate.

5. Fantasizing about someone else, while with your sex partner, is a form of cheating.

6. Couples should resolve emotional problems before handling sexual problems.

7. Older adults do not have to worry about getting HIV/AIDS or other sexually transmitted infections/diseases.

All of these statements are "false." Throughout this book, these sexual myths will be debunked and their importance explained. Understanding these beliefs and why they are false will help you to develop an *Authentic Sex Life*.

INTRODUCTION

As I go about my daily life, I often encounter strangers while I'm attending various functions, walking in the woods, and waiting: waiting at the supermarket, waiting for transportation, waiting for appointments. These are occasions when many of us look to people around us to make the time pass quickly. If we strike up a conversation and they find out I'm a sexologist working on a book, the obvious question I hear is, "What's the title?" When I answer *"Does Sex Have an Expiration Date?"* they automatically respond to the question with some version of "Yes" or "No." And for those who are unsure, "Does it?" The exchange often launches a fascinating monologue of disclosures. Sexually detailed stories quickly fill my ear, and related questions always follow—enough material to generate several books.

Here's the gist of a conversation I had with a woman at the local farmer's market. She began:

> I'm 60 years old; I've been married for 35 years. I love my husband, although our sex* life has become rather boring and almost non-existent. I wasn't depressed until I lost my desire for sex, and now I'm on antidepressants. Honestly, I think they're making me feel worse. I miss waking up to my body craving sex and our early years of intimate passion.

Her eyes begged for an explanation. I told her she should first get a thorough physical examination, and then we exchanged cards. She made me promise to let her know when my book was published.

This is a typical case, suggesting various circumstances that may be contributing to her lack of desire:

- At 60 years old, she probably is experiencing low estrogen and testosterone.
- After 35 years of marriage, her husband's face is most likely not enough to turn her on, as it might have done in the early stages of their relationship.
- Sex can become boring if the physical expression of love is limited to a routine sequence of all-too-familiar activities.
- Her depression could be a result of hormone imbalance and/or her response to lost desire for sex.
- A side effect of her antidepressants may well be an even lower libido.*

Some of you might resonate with one or more of her concerns. Yet I've heard many other stories, often from women who honestly felt they never really enjoyed sex. Menopause becomes a great excuse for stopping, and yet these women still love their partners. I realized it was important to honor all these women's needs, and so I developed the *Ageless Sex* philosophy: the physical expression of intimacy taking into consideration emotional needs, aging bodies, and health challenges. This philosophy incorporates several concepts:

- **Authentic Sex Life***: To recognize and honor how one feels about their sexuality and consciously act on it.
- **Personal Path to Pleasure***: A person's pattern and style of creating sexual pleasure with an ever-changing body, together with a partner or solo.
- **Conscious Coupling***: Living an *Authentic Sex Life* within a relationship, taking into consideration everyone's sexual needs. This might also mean not expressing oneself sexually or not very often.

This book provides guidelines and exercises to help you live this *Conscious Coupling* lifestyle. Why *Conscious Coupling?* Few couples discuss their sexual expectations before committing to a relationship. Honestly, in the early stages of your marriage or relationship it may have felt like sex came naturally. After all, you were most likely still in lust, fired by your "sex hormones," and propelled by the early stages of love plus novelty. But things change, and couples need to recognize and discuss these changes. The principle behind *Conscious Coupling* is to live an *Authentic Sex Life* within your relationship, regardless of what changes unfold over the years.

What Is Menopause?

Let me start with a mini-primer on menopause, since this is a major underlying cause of older women's concerns regarding their libido. Natural menopause occurs when menstrual periods stop permanently as part of a women's aging. The process starts when the ovaries begin to gradually stop producing hormones involved in reproduction. Ultimately the decline of estrogen levels along with the cessation of progesterone when official menopause sets in, plus the gradual reduction of testosterone due to aging, create a significant imbalance of hormones that affect various parts of the body.

The lowering of estrogen levels can start several years prior to official menopause and proceed past the official date of menopause, since small quantities of this hormone continue to be produced by the adrenal glands, fat cells, and hypothalamus section of the brain. This process can cause the variety of symptoms associated with menopause, and so the term *menopausal women** used in this book refers to the entire course of menopause:

- Peri-menopause: occurs 10-13 years prior to menopause, usually starting in a woman's 40s, but can be as early as mid-30s when hormones begin to fluctuate. Average length is four years, but may last only a few months or continue for as long as 10 years.
- Menopause: officially occurs on the day a woman has had no menstrual period for 12 consecutive months. In the United States, the average age this occurs is 51.

- Post-menopause: the years after official menopause.
- Induced menopause: Occurs before natural menopause when the ovaries are removed, or are damaged from radiation or treatment by specific medication. The sudden, artificial onset of menopause often causes symptoms similar to those attributed to the post-menopause time frame, but instead of easing into this transition it is an abrupt shift.

The Interaction of the Sex Hormones

Testosterone (T), thought to be directly responsible for the sex drive*, is produced in women's ovaries, adrenal glands, and fat cells. That hormone is usually associated with men, but women produce it also—in smaller amounts. The ovaries continue to manufacture T even past menopause. But the aging process that lowers T levels starts in the woman's mid 20s. By menopause, the levels have dropped dramatically.

T works in relation with estrogen to create the complicated process of the wanting of sex. So the balance of these sex hormones is directly affected by the fluctuating levels of estrogen due to menopause and the changing levels of T due to the aging process. And because these levels are constantly changing, the symptoms associated with these sex hormones are continually being affected.

Sexuality Changes Over Time

My choice of "low libido issues" as subject for this book was an easy decision. Concerns about female desire and arousal* were the ones most often voiced when I spoke with menopausal women. Many complained of a waning sexual interest, resulting in desire discrepancy* between partners. This is the number one issue that sex therapists report hearing in their office, regardless of client age.[1] It is also considered to be the most difficult to resolve.

As an older graduate student, I examined libido issues both statistically and personally. At times, I too felt my interest in sex waning. When during the investigative phase of my dissertation I gathered women in focus groups to discuss their libido and arousal, I was privy to some extremely informative testimonies. It seemed to confirm what all the media are discussing and the pharmaceutical companies are hoping to cash in on: many menopausal women report having lost their interest, their wish, their desire for sex. Informally, I have also spoken with andropausal* men. Some of them suffer a similar problem in silence, often too embarrassed to admit to lack of desire.

Does Sex Have an Expiration Date?

The scenarios vary, but the outcome—decreased interest in sex or decreased sexual desire—is experienced by many older women. The cause might be physiological: a side effect of drugs, hormonal changes, menopause, physical body challenges. Or it might be psychological: a long-term relationship has lost its spark, there's boredom in the bedroom, or emotional stress distracts their attention. And for many women, both physiological and psychological causes may be present and interact with each other. Whatever the cause, the end result is often the same: the body shuts down its desire for sex. In some instances it is an understandable response, especially when pain is involved. The pressing question might just be, "Does sex have an expiration date?" For some menopausal women, it feels like there is one. Hormonal changes caused by cessation of menses or by childbirth[2] or hysterectomy, side effects of medication, physical and psychological effects of aging, pain (e.g., general, dyspareunia,* vulvodynia*), dryness, chronic vaginal and urinary infections, stress, boredom and relationship problems—all can negatively impact a woman's libido and capacity for arousal.

Can I Get a Magic Pill? Does One Exist?

Often I hear women say, "I wish there was a magic pill,"[3] but in my opinion, we can't expect that one drug can cure a problem with different root causes. It is why many remedies may work for some women and not others. Pills, patches, creams (bio-identical, FDA approved and OTC) for supplemental hormones, and laser therapy are all treatments that have the potential to alleviate severe dryness, which may be related to vulvovaginal atrophy (VVA).* Even Viagra (off-label)[4] is prescribed by some gynecologists to encourage genital blood flow.

VVA affects almost 50%[5] of postmenopausal women. Symptoms include severe dryness, irritation, soreness, and pain, plus urinary incontinence, frequency, and urgency. If you suffer from one or more of these symptoms, you have several options to consider. The least invasive is the *Vaginal Renewal*™ program, which is further described on the book's website and relies on special non-estrogen-based creams and self-massage to rejuvenate the vaginal walls. This is an excellent alternative for women not interested in using estrogen-based products, especially if these women have been treated with chemotherapeutic agents used in the treatment of breast and other hormone-dependent cancers.

Supplemental estrogen is another option. If you are considering using estrogen, you need to discuss with your doctor the pros and cons of the various types of products to determine which is the best option for your symptoms and is also compatible with your medical history. Be aware most insurance companies do not reimburse for hormone therapy.

A pill or cream form of DHEA (dehydroepiandrosterone) can be purchased over the counter. This substance converts to testosterone and estrogen, and has the ability to raise these levels. Therefore it is important to consult your physician prior to use, especially if you have an estrogen-dependent cancer. The various treatments will be discussed in detail plus the list will be kept up to date on the book's website.

Additional non-invasive approaches such as explicit sex videos, print or pictorial erotica, sex toys/aids, personal erotic fantasies, and the like may also be used effectively as sexual triggers to jumpstart your arousal system. One reason for the success of *Fifty Shades of Grey* is that many women credit the books and movies with reviving their libido. (Chapter 6 will present these non-invasive approaches in more detail.)

Mindfulness meditation, yoga, and acupuncture are shown to help women who self-define as low libido. Chapter 7 discusses how each modality has the potential to impact women's interest in sex. In addition, the book's website lists various meditation tutorials.

Talk Therapy or Drugs?

Among sex professionals, some believe that libido and arousal issues can be remedied only with drug therapy. Others feel that change in libido and arousal is a natural part of aging. They believe it is pointless to research any pharmaceutical remedies, and concerned people should look for help only through talk therapies. My experience has led me to believe that women must be educated regarding their sexual health, and then given choices so they can ultimately decide for themselves which methods are best to create pleasure within an *Authentic Sex Life. Ageless Sex* is not an impossible concept, and this book provides multiple approaches to creating it.

Sex might not have been on your radar for a while now, and you may have absolutely no interest in rekindling a desire for it (in which case you probably weren't the one who purchased this book). Or perhaps the title resonated with your hope for reawakening your sex life, or you wanted to learn how to save your sexless relationship. If your committed partner handed you this book, then it is likely that he is trying to get his sexual needs met, and he wants that from you, not an outsider. He's probably hoping this book will help. It isn't unusual for men to confide in me that they are baffled by their wives' attitude toward sex: "I can't believe she thinks I can stay in this marriage if I have to give up sex," or, "I can't even talk to her about the situation, let alone ask for sex…. It's the elephant in the bedroom." I suspect the elephant has free rein of the entire house, since problems with sex affect all aspects of a relationship, and vice versa.

If you are in a committed relationship and have no interest in reviving your sex life, the information presented here will give you a better understanding of your situation and may help you to validate your personal choice. I suggest a variety of options, including the choice to be asexual* or just occasionally being sexual, while still addressing your partner's needs and honoring your own.

Not for Women Only

I originally planned to write a book for women so they could better understand what was happening to their bodies and how to remedy the situation. But coupled heterosexual sex is a collaborative process, and men were continually asking me for information regarding their partners' sexuality. And when women approached me with questions, they referred to their specific problems and issues in conjunction with how their partner's responses and problems were impacting their sexual relationship.

Reminder: this book is based on heterosexual couples' stories, since those are the couples who mostly comprise my practice, and the women who were in my focus groups spoke mainly about husbands as sex partners. The women I chatted with out in public always spoke about male partners also, therefore my usage of male pronouns throughout the book. However, the *Sexual Pleasure Model* and the information along with exercises can be helpful for all women reading this book.

Throughout these chapters you will find anecdotes: composite stories told to me by participants in my focus groups, seminars, and those who share their experiences during "waiting in line" conversations. All of the stories have one thing in common: they reference sex and sexual desire. And that's because sexual desire is a major source of conversation among menopausal women. When I become part of these conversations and women learn I'm a sexologist, they immediately want to know what that means. Once they understand my role as adult sex educator/consultant, the floodgates open and then the discussion often focuses on their feelings of low libido. I have also included composite sessions of my clients (in-person and via telecommunications) so readers can get a better sense of how to communicate and negotiate with their partner.

Medical Schools Lack Sex...Education

It quickly became clear to me that the women who felt they had a low libido either didn't know who to approach with their difficulties or they were uncomfortable discussing their sexual needs and problems with their health care provider. Unfortunately, even if they had done so, they might not have received much help. As of 2003, medical students were reported typically to devote an average of only 3-10 hours total over 4 years to human sexuality courses.[6] Even in 2013, an article on the current and future status of sexuality education in North American medical schools concluded,

> Many sexual health education programs in medical schools are focused on prevention of unwanted pregnancy and sexually transmitted infection. Educational material on sexual function and dysfunction, female sexuality, abortion, and sexual minority groups is generally scant or absent.[7]

Gynecologists might be better educated regarding your problem, but be aware: that doesn't mean they are nonjudgmental when discussing your concerns. I have spoken with women who have been shamed into thinking their sexual practices are deviant or were told their unexplained pain must be all in their head.

After speaking with countless menopausal women and taking into account my personal experience, I now realize it is difficult finding a doctor who specializes in pelvic pain, libido/arousal concerns, and other menopause-related health issues. I have created a website specifically to keep an up-to-date listing of directories, organizations, and doctors that specialize in menopausal women's needs. A word of caution: There are health care providers out there who will exploit women's problems, and sometimes it is difficult to tell whether their solutions would be best for your needs or whether they are just trying to peddle their products. If any of the health professionals you consult with seem uncomfortable discussing your concerns, or make you feel shamed when discussing your sexual issues, mores, and/or practices (let alone the idea of sexual pleasure at your age), keep searching until you find a nonjudgmental professional.

My own nonjudgmental manner was developed through my training at the Institute for Advanced Study of Human Sexuality (IASHS). The Institute introduced me to the term "sex-positive," an approach to sex and sexuality that is essential for a sexologist. Dr. Carol Queen, founder of the Center for Sex & Culture in San Francisco and graduate of IASHS, provides an excellent interpretation of what the Institute means by the term sex-positive:[8]

- A way to acknowledge that human sexuality is diverse and broad. There is no one definition of *normal.**

- Non-judgmental, or in any case it asks us to be aware of (and be in control of) our [sic] judgements.

- A foe of shaming others about sexual (and gendered) matters, including children.

- A way to acknowledge that we should have certain sexual rights, including the right to comprehensive, appropriate, pleasure-inclusive, positive sex education.

- A construct that invites us to acknowledge that pretty much any fully consensual behavior might be right for someone, and pretty much nothing is right for everyone.

- An idea that can't be fully expressed outside of an atmosphere/context of consent.* Informed, non-coercive consent.

- A term that can include anyone, including virgins, asexuals, people who have been abused, people who have never had pleasurable or even good sex—because it does not describe the sex they do/don't have, it describes their *attitude* about sexual diversity and people's sexual rights. (And, of course, it may be a tool to open the door to much more positive sex—but only if it's what they want.)

- More than anything, a way to critique our current culture—which clearly is not sex-positive. I express the critique like this: What would it take for our culture to be fully sex-positive? What are the elements that would get us there? (I invite you to think about that question—it is a valuable lens in a personal context and in activist work.)

- A notion that gives us access to true respect for other people's sexualities.

I have adopted the second point—to view anything pertaining to an individual's sexuality without judgment—and have used it in all my interactions with people. This has given individuals the comfort necessary to confide their deepest secrets to me without shame.

To instill this understanding of sexuality in its students, IASHS requires them to complete their process-oriented SAR[9] (Sexual Attitude Reassessment/Restructuring). A condensed version has since been incorporated into the curriculum of numerous medical schools. The

University of Minnesota Medical School and Rutgers University's Robert Wood Johnson Medical School are two institutions offering a SAR, but unfortunately it is not yet a mandatory course for future doctors.

During the SAR process, I examined my attitudes, beliefs, biases, and values regarding sexuality. This was key to advancing my comfort level with the many variations in sexual expression that I would encounter as a practicing sexologist.

Women have mentioned how my nonjudgmental approach and open attitude towards sexuality have given them the freedom to express their concerns honestly and without embarrassment. They have felt comfortable asking me, "What is low libido? Can I be tested for it? Is it a natural part of the aging process? Should I take drugs to change it? I haven't had sex in years, and I don't miss it. Is that normal?" Hence my research leads me to ask: Why are so many menopausal women desperately demanding, "Where has my libido gone?"

It Gets Better

Our bodies seem to talk back to us when we are under stress, injured, or infirm. Even as we age and travel through various stages of life, our bodies speak to us. But we don't always listen or want to listen, especially when it comes to sex. We assume sex will remain the same forever—thank goodness it doesn't!

Research has shown that for some people, sex gets better with age. In a survey described in the *American Journal of Medicine* during 2012, women over 80 said they had a greater frequency of sexual satisfaction than did younger women.[10] What were those older respondents referring to when they said "better"?

In my focus groups for women, there was always a subgroup who couldn't imagine "not" wanting sex. They shared willingly much information regarding their sexuality, happily discussing the best sexual practices for dealing with their aging bodies and those of their partners. They exchanged details about the latest lubricants, moisturizers, and sex toys/aids*—and most interestingly how aging has actually expanded their delight in sexual intimacy. They now spend more time enjoying a wider variety of sexual expressions than when their hormones were raging, driving them straightaway to the finish line (orgasm*). It was these women who contributed to the development of the *Personal Path to Pleasure*, which is described within these chapters.

As a celebrity example, *Brady Bunch* mom Florence Henderson sure wasn't living in a 1970s TV show—complete with single beds—as of 2015. "I actually have a friend with benefits!" the late 81-year-old actress told *Closer Weekly*.[11] Henderson, divorced and widowed, said her sex buddy was a chiropractor in Fort Lauderdale, Florida. "There is no age limit on the enjoyment of sex. It keeps getting better" Henderson told *Closer*. "You learn to do things with more experience, intelligence, and the ability to choose more wisely."

The prime-time matriarch, whose family comedy *The Brady Bunch* originally aired from 1969 to 1974, was clearly onto something important.

Viewing Libido

Low libido is a difficult concept to understand; even healthcare professionals cannot come to an agreement on how best to view and treat it. Some professionals distrust medical remedies, and others turn immediately to drugs for treatment.

I believe how we view libido plays a large role in how we treat it. Trained to look at low libido in a holistic manner, I make suggestions that vary depending upon the issues leading a woman to self-define as being low. Influences that can lead someone to report the misleading term of *low libido* include cultural attitudes regarding "normal" sex drive/sexual desire, body imagery, shame, medical factors, and the condition of her relationship, as well as a good deal of misinformation or just plain lack of information. Simply being stressed out about one's circumstances can affect hormone levels, which can lower desire for sex, thus adding another layer of complications to this already complex situation.

Women describe their libido as being low for a variety of reasons, and sometimes their frustrated sex partners confer this status upon them. Below you will find some scenarios women associate with low libido. These sexual situations are labeled low libido because they all contribute to a similar outcome: a lack of interest in sex.

But first, just what is SEX (the activity)? In this book, you get to define it for yourself. Do not be surprised if you change the scope of your definition once you discover your *Authentic Sex Life* through this book.

Comments I hear from women who think they have a low libido include:

- My partner wants sex more than I do.
- My partner wants sex all the time.
- Our sex life is boring.
- My orgasms have become a blip.
- I always have pain during intercourse.
- I always have pain after intercourse.
- I miss my fantasies.
- He's so fat/out of shape, he doesn't turn me on any longer.
- I'm so fat/out of shape/saggy/wrinkled, he couldn't possibly be really interested in me anymore.
- I no longer feel horny.
- I miss the feeling of longing for him.
- If I never have sex again, I won't miss it.
- He was never a great lover.
- Once I get going, sex is usually fine, but I have to remember this when I'm not in the mood.
- Old women don't do that anymore.
- I'm past the age to want sex.
- I never really enjoyed sex.

Some of these statements seem to have little in common. However, they share one important element: they each have the ability to change your interest in sex. Some even lead to self-fulfilling thoughts and others perpetuate a negative feedback loop.

This book is created to provide you with the information needed to develop your *Authentic Sex Life*, even if that involves choosing asexuality. Unique solutions are presented to allow asexuality to be a valid personal choice and still honor both you and your partner's needs.

The suggestions in future chapters can expand your horizons when it comes to expressions of intimacy and the potential for sexual satisfaction. Summarizing results from the 2012 Sexual Satisfaction in Women Survey, first author Dr. Susan E. Trompeter concluded:

> In this study, sexual activity [here, meaning intercourse] was not always necessary for sexual satisfaction. Those who were not sexually active may have achieved sexual satisfaction through touching, caressing, or other intimacies developed over the course of a long relationship.... Emotional and physical closeness to the partner may be more important than experiencing orgasm. A more positive approach to female sexual health focusing on sexual satisfaction may be more beneficial to women than a focus limited to female sexual activity or dysfunction.[12]

Within this book you will also find exercises to help motivate you to be sexually active if you decide to revive your sex life, but you do need to trust the process and yourself.

Sex and Your Relationship

The forthcoming recommendations for exploring your *Authentic Sex Life* are based on an assumption that you have an otherwise healthy relationship or one that was vital prior to your waning desire for sex. But ultimately there are many aspects of your life, including cultural and family attitudes, health challenges, life circumstances, and body awareness that impact how you respond to your partner's sexual advances or initiate sex yourself. If you have serious relationship issues independent of sex, you may want to see a couples' therapist.

I want to share with you a caution that I often impart to my clients. If the advice and strategies that I lay out here help you solve sexual and relationship issues (and I sincerely hope they will), it is likely that those solutions will come at the expense of the status quo; not only will your relationship change, but you as an individual will go through some changes. Change can be scary, but—and this part is sometimes hard to keep in mind—such exploration can help you forge a more *Authentic Sexual Life*.

As you read, you will occasionally come across non-traditional recommendations. Essentially I am suggesting a new way of being in relationship, and even a new way of being you, one that allows for more openness and a greater regard for both yourself and your partner. Please research the material thoroughly, examine your feelings regarding my suggestions, and decide whether the advice could serve you, and ultimately your relationship.

Expanding your definition of sex and the expression of your intimate connection can be tremendously invigorating to your relationship. Honoring both you and your partner's sexual interests and needs, which can include your or your partner's choice of asexuality, can help you create a more conscious coupling.

As a sexologist, I respect all forms of legal sexual behaviors and non-coercive consensual choices. The IASHS issues a list of Sexual Human Rights that includes, "the right to sexual self-determination."[13] I interpret this to mean that we all have a fundamental right to express ourselves sexually and, conversely, an equal right *not* to express ourselves sexually.

A Sexless Marriage

During the focus groups and individual interviews I conducted while doing research for my BA thesis and PhD dissertation, most of the coupled women who were not interested in having sex had concerns about how their partner might react. Men seem to confirm these concerns. These are some of the ways couples reported typical grievances:

She: He only wants sex at night, so I pretend to be sleeping when he gets into bed.

He: She's always tired.

She: I never really liked having sex—besides, I'm already 60. He's oversexed, still wants it, and he's almost 75!

He: She never wants sex anymore, but I still need it. She thinks we're too old. I don't want to cheat, but what can I do?

She: I think he finally got the hint I'm not interested, but I'm afraid he might find it elsewhere. I guess it's okay if he doesn't bring home any germs.

He: I've had too many rejections. I've given up on sex with my wife.

She: He keeps pestering me for sex and I eventually give in. That is the only time we have sex. Can't wait for it to be over, I'm so not into it.

He: She just lays there and doesn't respond as I pound her. Then pushes me off when I'm finished.

She: I really like it when he holds me. I'm too embarrassed to tell him how much sex hurts. He's always in a rush.

He: She only wants to cuddle. That is not enough for me.

She: Every time we kiss he tries to feel my breasts and then I stop him, since I know he'll want more.

He: She won't let me even touch her.

These men are expressing their frustration: they love their wives but don't know how to reconcile their need for sex with her diminished desire for it. Many of my male clients say that they no longer experience even non-erotic touch from their partners. They divulge their fears that they may eventually stray or request a divorce. Their sexual needs are pressing, and they have no idea how to resolve the situation. They want to focus their sexual desire on their partners, but this has become impossible.

Discrepancy in desire for sex is one of the major complaints sex therapists deal with in their practice. For some couples, this disparity has led to a sexless and oftentimes a touchless marriage. If they do consult with a therapist, they will most likely be met with one that works within the confines of the traditional marriage model. However, with the rise in divorce and infidelity there are a growing number of therapists offering progressive, more non-traditional recommendations (link to the book's website for directory of therapists), but usually only after a trust has been broken—that is, an affair has been exposed. To protect the commitment bond, I will introduce in Chapter 8 guidelines for developing a contemporary intimate relationship and avoiding the heartache of one partner cheating on the other and/or filing for divorce. All couples can follow these recommendations, whether you have an extreme desire discrepancy or are interested in exploring a more flexible approach to your relationship.

The combination of information, exercises, and treatments suggested in this book will help you choose whether to revive your libido, abstain from sexual contact intentionally, or keep the status quo, whatever it might be. If you choose abstinence (or a modified version of it), the information in this book will guide you in making it work for both you and your partner. This mutuality is important, because when we are in a relationship, our choice to abstain doesn't affect us alone; it affects our partner as well. If he is feeling estranged, he may be considering getting his sexual needs met elsewhere. And you may desire to maintain an emotionally intimate connection with him but are simply not open to a sexual relationship.

When selecting revival, simply reading this text might not be enough for some women to change their responses or behavior—the exercises are designed to facilitate sexual pleasure and satisfaction. You may feel awkward performing some of these activities at first, but only you can decide how much you wish to challenge yourself. Please do not allow anyone to coerce you into trying the exercises; they will only be beneficial if you are truly interested in transforming your present motivation for sex.

What's "Normal," Anyway?

I often remind my clients that there really is no *normal* when it comes to sexual expression and the desire for sex, although there are certainly traditional styles of sexual behavior, and traditional ways of relating to one's partner. I prefer viewing sexuality as points along a continuum, and we all fall somewhere along this continuum.

For example, I recall a conversation I had with a man in his 80s when he described a comical routine in bed with his sex partner. He mentioned that the sex lasted several hours and-neither partner had an orgasm, but they laughed a lot, especially when they awkwardly changed positions to alleviate pain. Then, with a huge grin he said, "At the end, we agreed that we hadn't had that much fun in a long while."

I contrast that conversation with one I had on my way to a sexology conference. It was the taxi driver's good fortune that we were stuck in traffic while traveling from my Philadelphia home to the airport. We started with small talk, but the conversation quickly progressed to sex when he found out my conference destination and profession. He hesitated before asking, "My wife said women over 50 do not have sex. Is this true?" His voice sounded as if even he found this difficult to believe, but he wanted an expert's opinion and confirmation. I assured him this was not true, and added that perhaps his wife had read that information somewhere or heard it from one of her friends. I suggested he tell his wife to consult a health care professional so she could hear the truth from someone with formal training, and perhaps get advice about her own desires for sex.

Another point on the continuum is occupied by Frances, who passed away at 100½ years of natural causes. She was a regular contributor at my Erotic Literary Salon in Philadelphia, and her mere presence at the gathering dispelled myths regarding aging and sexuality. She read the following piece at the Salon when she was in her early 90s, about a man who eventually became her boyfriend for almost seven years, until he died at the age of 98; she was two years younger and at 96 moved on to other boyfriends. This piece is also included in *SenSexual: A Unique Anthology 2013*, an ebook dedicated to Frances, in which you can read more of her sex memoir essays.[14]

There he was, the man, standing by the pool of our senior community. My eyes stood still and my breath slowed down. I hadn't seen a white-haired man who could touch my heart for almost a lifetime. We reached for each other and agreed to meet the next week.

Without shame, I lay naked on the bed, eagerly separating my legs as the man knelt before me. My body warmed in a new way. Ripples of movement ran through me, and music by Vivaldi.

My skin smoothed out and was flooded with rosy coloring. I was a painting by Rubens and the man said I was beautiful.

The evening Frances read this piece, she at first forgot to mention the title, but then she blurted it out: "First Date." The audience gasped, and she replied, "We're old, we don't have that much time."

These stories embody the upbeat and positive tone I have adopted for the material in this book. Especially as we age, the bed can sometimes be a traumatic place full of mishaps and baggage. But if our time together is about enjoying the pleasures of the moment and is filled with laughter, it is difficult to have a bad experience no matter what the outcome.

You may not be where Frances is, and you may never want to go there. Maybe you resonate more with the woman who approached me at the market to say how much she loved her husband yet bemoaned her lack of desire for sex and was hoping to get it back. But here's what matters: Your place on the continuum of sexuality is yours, but it is not a fixed position. Consider this book a catalyst that will guide you on a journey to:

1. More fully examine the depths of your own experience to see where you wish to be on the continuum.
2. Make a decision about whether you want to become more conscious regarding your own sexuality.
3. Develop a more *Conscious Coupling* relationship.

Wherever you land and wherever it may take you, I hope this book will support you in the process in discovering your *Authentic Sex Life.*

1

LIBIDO, AROUSAL, AND DESIRING SEX (OR NOT)

Your *Personal Path to Pleasure*!

When you are past the age of procreation, and especially when the effects of menopause and body challenges have caused havoc with your sexual responses, particularly sexual *motivation*, it is easy to forget that having sex is all about pleasure. During my research and in my practice as a sexologist, I have come to realize that each woman has her own unique method for creating the wanting of sex, the experience of sexual pleasure, and the outcome of sexual satisfaction as she defines it. This process is not a fixed approach and is impacted by many circumstances including the demands of daily life, state of her relationship, and body challenges. As a result, your typical sexual style from your younger years might have become compromised and you may be unsure how or even whether to proceed back to being sexually active again.

In the process of discovering your *Personal Path to Pleasure*, you will learn the unique ways that your body develops an interest in sex and what has led you to believe you have a low libido. The *Sexual Pleasure Model* is a template for exploring your *Personal Path to Pleasure*. This model includes various styles of creating pleasure such as outercourse,* expanded sex,* and sexplay,* all of which will be discussed in detail in Chapter 6. This approach focuses on sexual satisfaction that may be independent of the "traditional orgasm," or may even exclude orgasm for gratification altogether. It also introduces a spiritual[1] component that some women have found to be an integral part of their experience. The *Personal Path to Pleasure* is as unique as the individual woman who is interested in experiencing sexual pleasure.

The Sexual Pleasure Model

1. **Sexual Trigger**
    a. <u>Unconscious</u> –
        i. Sex drive
            1. Emotional (spontaneous erotic thoughts/fantasies)
            2. Physical (spontaneous physical sensations)
    b. <u>Conscious</u>
        i. External stimuli (fabricated fantasies, provocative situations, stimulation of body, use of explicit sex material)
        ii. Mental motivation (inner state of psyche)

2. **Sexual Arousal** - Interest in sex (physical)
3. **Sexual Desire** - Interest in sex (emotional)

    OR

2. **Sexual Desire** - Interest in sex (emotional)
3. **Sexual Arousal** - Interest in sex (physical)

4. **Sexual Satisfaction**
    a. <u>Sexual pleasuring behaviors</u> (sexplay, expanded sex, outercourse)
        i. Traditional orgasm
        ii. Non-orgasmic
    b. <u>Spiritual/Sacred component</u> (Neo-Tantra techniques)
        i. Energy orgasm*
        ii. Non-orgasmic

This is not a linear model, since arousal can fade during a sexual session. When this occurs, conscious sexual triggers need to be applied to activate it.

The term *libido* is not used in this model since it is the combination of sex drive and sexual desire, although many women include sexual arousal when they are referring to their libido. It is the interplay of libido and arousal that produces the wanting of sex.

Why Would YOU Want Sex?

It is important to remember that even a healthy sex life ebbs and flows, since the motivating elements are always shifting. How might your motivations be affecting your present feelings about your libido? It may be useful to recognize your past incentives for engaging in sexual activity and note changes.

Go through the list below and check your past and present reasons for acting sexually. You can mark more than one and include additional incentives to personalize the list.

Motivating Factors for Having Sex

	N/A	PAST	PRESENT
• for affection	___	___	___
• for duty	___	___	___
• for excitement	___	___	___
• as a gift	___	___	___
• for money	___	___	___
• to relieve loneliness	___	___	___
• to experience sexual pleasure	___	___	___
• to have an orgasm	___	___	___
• to be emotionally intimate with a partner	___	___	___
• to please a partner	___	___	___
• to please yourself	___	___	___
• to relieve tension	___	___	___
• to revitalize yourself	___	___	___

	N/A	PAST	PRESENT
• to induce sleep	_____	_____	_____
• to relieve boredom	_____	_____	_____
• to apologize	_____	_____	_____
• to feel good about yourself (more attractive, desired, feminine)	_____	_____	_____
• to feel loved	_____	_____	_____
• to feel powerful	_____	_____	_____
• to feel less anxious or guilty about how infrequently you are having sex	_____	_____	_____
• to feel "normal"	_____	_____	_____

It is common for couples who marry for love to express their affection and to become emotionally intimate through sexual behaviors. These initial motivating factors expand if you and your partner experience sexual pleasure. Pleasure is a very powerful response, and at some point it becomes difficult to tease out the true motivating factors for couples having sex. These motivations can become a combination of both the wanting and offering of physical sensations, be based on one specific reason or a combination of several factors.

After years of marriage, you might take your affection for each other for granted or demonstrate it differently. At present, your expression of love might be reflected in other activities that could have surpassed the pleasure you received from sexplay. If you instigated sexplay to "relieve…" or "induce…" various states of being, your lack of sexual pleasure probably has you relying on other techniques to "relieve" or "induce."

It is not uncommon for menopausal women to experience vaginal and orgasmic changes that impact their sexual pleasure negatively. Therefore, relying on sexual behaviors to express your feelings or using them to "relieve…" or "induce…" might no longer be a comfortable solution.

Am I Asexual*? Should I Be? Is That Okay?

By contrast, you might refrain from acting sexually because of the impact the following factors may be having on your physical, emotional, and sexual health. Some of these issues can become exacerbated by menopause, aging, and health challenges. You can add to this list to personalize it:

- exhaustion from insomnia and/or hot flashes
- lack of internal sexual cues (thoughts, fantasies)
- change in physical feelings of arousal
- vaginal/vulva pain
- difficulties in reaching orgasm
- physical problems
- partner's physical problems
- anger towards partner
- sexual boredom
- feeling inept
- feeling that sex is unfulfilling
- being stressed out
- feeling neglected
- sensing that your sexual partner is not listening to your needs
- side effects from prescribed or over-the-counter medication(s) (OTCs)
- fear of incontinence during intercourse or orgasm
- depression/malaise

Maggie, the woman I met at the farmer's market, used to love sex. But during menopause she experienced a sense of melancholy, and about the same time she lost her desire for sex. Her physician prescribed antidepressants in hopes that they would alleviate her malaise. Unfortunately, one of the side effects of her particular antidepressant was decreased libido. She was referred to me because of her libido changes, and we started by exploring what brought on her initial malaise. She said, "I feel out of control emotionally ever since I went through menopause." When I encouraged her to give an example of what set her off, she replied, "Situations or things my husband used to do that I would disregard now seem impossible to ignore. You know those little things like leaving the toilet seat up, using his fingers instead of a knife to push his food onto his fork. I guess I'm not picking my battles as well as I used to."

We discussed using meditation and exercise on a regular basis to help regulate her moods. But most importantly we discussed triggers to jump-start her desire for sex. The combination had her smiling again when she realized that the mild depression, feeling of low libido, plus medication had created a negative cycle, which actually ended when she stopped taking the medication with her doctor's approval and followed her *Personal Path to Pleasure* to again create the desire for sex.

Multiple approaches to reviving an interest in sex are described in this book, but at no time should you feel coerced into doing so. (Note: It is *extremely* important that you never stop taking medications or change dosage of your antidepressant without consulting a medical professional.)

Your story might be quite different from Maggie's. Maybe you never experienced pleasure from sex; for you, menopause might be experienced as a relief. You no longer miss the unwanted urges, since having sex was never very gratifying. You may think, "I don't need to have sex anymore. I never enjoyed it, so why should I start again?" This may be a good time to consider the reasons for your original lack of pleasure, since it may be possible for you to enjoy sex now, despite expectations and past experiences. If you skipped over the points above, I encourage you to evaluate what could be your incentives for having acted sexually in the past and review the various factors that may be impacting your sexual health negatively. You might be one of those women who never experienced an orgasm or one that was worth mentioning. For many women orgasm is an incentive to have sex. (There is a section in Chapter 6 devoted exclusively to orgasm.) And importantly, you will need to consider your husband, and how choosing asexuality affects your relationship.

You may have already "chosen" asexuality without knowing it had a name. As a couple, you might have gradually slipped into a sexless marriage, like Julia and her husband Jim. Julia told me,

I read an article in the Internet about sexless marriages and realized I was living in one…. In the early years of our marriage, it seemed that foreplay lasted for hours—we cuddled a lot. Now Jim rarely gets hard, so he stopped wanting sex and then I also lost interest. I miss the cuddling.

"I Just Don't Care Anymore"

Or perhaps you can relate to part of the following story. Evana's total lack of interest in sex started in her 50s with a series of unrelated events: the death of her mother, her partner Mike's extreme back pain, and then a vaginal infection exacerbated by severe dryness. After many months of abstinence, Mike's back problem had resolved and he was ready to resume having sex, but Evana felt as if someone "shut off the switch" for her, as she so bluntly stated. The loss of her desire for desire didn't actually distress her, but her husband's nagging did. He wanted sex again, but this was the furthest thing from her mind.

Like many women, Evana's life circumstances affected her sexual responses negatively. When she experienced no sexual feelings after an extended period of celibacy, she gave up. This created a cycle that ultimately left her feeling asexual.

Your interest may have declined for other reasons: sexual boredom, or perhaps because your feelings for your long-term partner became more familial than sexual. Sometimes a woman will tell me that she is most comfortable in her relationship, yet she has one curious but pressing complaint: "We love each other very much, we've become best friends, like brother and sister, but we don't have sex anymore." It is not unusual that desire for sex seems to vanish in these circumstances. (Sustaining an erotically charged relationship will be discussed in Chapter 4.)

Women with these varied complaints often assume their libido is low simply because they no longer experience the desire for sex. Similar to these women, you may have relied mainly on your innate physical sex drive (inner physical sensations such as tingling clitoris, pelvic congestion, and/or hardened nipples) to create what feels like an automatic interest in sex. But the body changes. The aging process, health challenges, medications, and hormonal fluctuations all affect this component of libido, and can create a risk for diminished sex drive.

A Broken System

To complicate matters further, it isn't really possible to examine how libido affects an interest in sex without bringing sexual arousal into the mix. Sexual arousal is the body's physical response to alluring sexual stimuli, fantasies, and internal trains of thought, or even provocative situations. As noted earlier, it is the interplay of libido and arousal that produces the wanting of sex. When this system breaks down—and that breakdown can occur at many stages—you need to do some sleuthing if you want to remedy the situation. Various influences such as hormonal fluctuations, aging, certain medical conditions, and/or medications can affect internal cues, cues that in the past translated to triggers for desiring sex.

I suggest you consult with your partner and ask his thoughts regarding your situation. Eyes and ears of another person who spends a lot of time with you can be most helpful. He might recall things you have forgotten or thought were irrelevant.

If you have experienced sudden or irregular response changes, these could also be a sign of the following medical conditions:

- diabetes
- kidney disease
- heart disease
- liver disease
- thyroid disease
- neurological disorders
- chemical addictions

I suggest you have a thorough physical examination by your health care provider before you make any major decisions regarding your *Authentic Sex Life*. One or more of these problems could be an underlying cause of your sexual concerns.

Oh, Those Hormones!

The combination of aging and hormonal changes can also affect the senses. The noted international figure in women's health, Dr. Alessandra Graziottin, is a trained medical sexologist, gynecologist, oncologist, and psychotherapist specializing in sexual issues. When she was interviewed in "The Evolution of Desire" for the Alexander Foundation for Women's Health,[2] she spoke about the role of hormones in stimulating desire:

- The skin and all our sensory organs are affected by hormones. Research shows that women have increased sensitivity to smell during ovulation. We are attracted to a mate because we like the way he smells, but as we age, our sensory response declines.
- Salivary secretion also diminishes with age and loss of estrogen. After menopause about 46 percent of women complain of dry mouth. This goes up to 62 percent if the women are on other medications.
- Taste is modulated by hormones, so when we grow older, even our experience of kissing or the taste of our partner's skin may change. Studies show that increased salivary secretion during arousal is a strong predictor of sexual enjoyment.

It's likely that in the past you consistently relied on at least one of these senses to create cues for wanting sex. Your mind converts these indicators of arousal into feelings of sexual desire and ultimately an interest in sex. In the absence of these signs you might very well have assumed your libido is low or even nonexistent, but it is actually your arousal system that is challenged.

Arousal!

Your body's arousal response is an extremely complex and sometimes self-protective reaction in women. Your response not only depends on physical or mental stimulation, but most importantly how the mind perceives and interprets the stimuli and then converts them to pleasure and an interest in sex. Or doesn't.

I overheard one participant in my sexuality and aging seminar explain her protective arousal system to another attendee:

> If I'm on deadline with a paper for school, no amount of kissing can turn me on. But one tiny kiss to the back of my neck while washing dishes, and we'll be waking up to a sink full of dirty ones.

Women who are being assaulted sexually have experienced physical signs of arousal such as lubrication, but they do not convert this to desire for sex. Yet women who give consent to role-playing scenes where they are being ravished not only become physically aroused but have a great interest in behaving sexually.

Desire for sex often creates physical sensations, and conversely the sensations that arousal produces may activate and enhance a woman's desire for sex—a sort of feedback loop. This interconnection is most intriguing and oftentimes confusing when trying to sleuth out where your lack of desire may originate. The following two scenarios illustrate how arousal and desire can intertwine in different sequences to create the wanting of sex:

(1) You're lying in the arms of your husband with no desire for sex, until you become aware that he is covering you with the lightest of kisses. He pays special attention to your hands and starts to suck on your fingers. This new sensation starts to wake up other areas of your body and you soon realize you are in the midst of enjoying sex. What started as a "Not tonight dear" evening became a "Take me now!" one. This scene shows how sensations of arousal could lead to the desire for sex.[3]

Or:

(2) You've just spent a glorious day with your husband walking the beach, picnicking, and then dancing under the stars. You built the intensity of your desire for your husband throughout the day by gazing into each other's eyes, smiling, occasionally holding hands, teasing, but intentionally never kissing. The desire to touch sexually was finally realized when you fell into each

other's arms after dinner. The erotically charged day had created intense arousal signals that had you wet and wanting by evening, ultimately leading to passionate sex.

These are wonderful scenarios when all systems are functioning properly. But as noted earlier, the complications of an aging body and hormonal fluctuations can alter the typical physical indicators for arousal. Your brain, which previously sent out signals of arousal when it converted a specific tweak to a turn-on, may not know what to do when your typical tweak or sensation doesn't feel the same. An added complication is when the brain does not respond to even familiar signals in its usual fashion, creating quite a conundrum when trying to distinguish among arousal and libido related problems.

Forgotten Triggers and Broken Links

The chain of physical triggers that worked for you in the past to create sexual desire and/or arousal may have links that are no longer connected. Here are a few examples of turn-ons where broken links might create a feeling of low libido. These do not apply to all women; it is possible that you may have different body connections that are no longer sending signals.

- Nipples can be an extremely sensitive area[4] for some women. If a woman depends on her nipple responsiveness to stimulate her interest in sex or create an orgasm and the brain no longer perceives a strong nipple sensation, arousal will probably be impaired.
- Some women become aroused when they have an awareness of a heavy or "full" vaginal sensation. (The walls of the vagina become swollen with blood due to sexual stimulation, which is normal.) If these women have poor circulation, this sensation might be minimized and they feel no desire for sex.
- Poor circulation can also diminish the engorgement of the clitoris. The various clitoral sensations such as tingling, throbbing, and fullness may be reduced, making it difficult to feel aroused. For some women, moreover, orgasm is the major motivation factor for

having sex, and poor circulation can make it more difficult to experience a traditional orgasm.

- Vaginal lubrication increases when the body is touched in a pleasurable manner. Four events could happen either separately or simultaneously to change this vaginal response.
  - o Nerves in the skin might react differently to touch.
  - o Hormonal imbalance can compromise communication between touch, brain, and the vagina at any given point.
  - o The touch of a woman's partner has changed and is not perceived as pleasurable. Sometimes this is because the man has altered his movements (from, for example, tremor or stroke), or there may be skin changes due to aging or medical conditions (e.g., dry skin).
  - o The vagina produces inadequate lubrication. This can have a number of causes, including estrogen deficiency, medications (OTC antihistamines are a common one), poor genital blood flow, and infections. If juiciness (wetness) was your turn-on, your brain will not register being aroused.

Surprisingly there are only three medically attested symptoms of menopause: hot flashes, vaginal dryness, and the cessation of menses. These happen because your ovaries no longer produce the sex hormones—estrogen and progesterone, and testosterone is produced in lower amounts due to aging. But a domino effect accounts for many other symptoms that can potentially occur as a result of these three primary ones, including:

- Fatigue

- Mood swings

- Migraines

- Depression

- Malaise

- Insomnia

- Genital pain

- Frequent urination

- Urinary incontinence

- Urinary tract infections

- Thinning of hair

- Difficulty concentrating

- Memory lapses

- Dizziness

- Anxiety

- Panic disorder

- Bloating

- Weight gain

- Allergies

- Joint pain

- Brittle nails

- Gum problems

- Muscle tension

- Tingling in the extremities

- Digestive problems

- Breast soreness/tenderness

- Irregular heartbeat

- Odor changes

- Osteoporosis

- Electric shock sensation in various locations in the body

I recall a day when I thought for certain the flu was upon me. I experienced almost 12 hours of sweating and chills, but no temperature and no other symptoms. At some point I realized these were non-stop hot flashes, and they disappeared as quickly as they had appeared. However, because I thought I was ill I missed a really important event; and that upset me.

There are several typical chain reactions that women have brought to my attention. It is not unusual for me to hear them complain about increased fatigue, and when asked about the quality of their sleep, they answer, "What sleep?" Insomnia, frequent urination, electric shock sensations, and—for some—purely night sweats/chills have them up every few hours, often unable to fall back asleep. These same women also complain of difficulty concentrating; no wonder, because their minds are exhausted. Another common complaint concerns body image, which can be influenced negatively when women experience thinning of hair, loss of skin tone, and/or digestive problems that can affect bloating and weight gain.

There are many combinations of symptoms initially set off by one or all three of the medically proven symptoms of menopause. Malaise and, at its worst, depression can set in when women feel they are not in control of these symptoms. And to make matters worse, the medications most often prescribed can have side effects of low libido.

Detecting Arousal: How Does HE Know?

Sometimes just being aware that these trigger changes can occur may help you to focus on other signs or figure out new tweaks to get yourself physically excited and in the mood. For example, your partner may misread your altered signs of arousal—like not lubricating—as an indication that you are not interested in sex, specifically intercourse. He may assume you are just going through the motions because of what some may refer to as "obligatory sex." He might be thinking, "She doesn't love me anymore … she doesn't desire me… she doesn't…." Because we're human, we all tend to take things personally, and feeling rejected is at the very heart of these issues. I encourage you to have a conversation with your partner about changes in your arousal pattern, and how compensating for these changes can be integrated into your sexplay*.

In addition to discussing physical cues with your partner, consider examining your own signs of arousal leading up to and including the traditional orgasm. Arousal can change with age and ultimately alter your experience of orgasm. The following questionnaire incorporates a list of typical signs of sexual response and orgasm taken from the standard Human Sexual Response Cycle (HSRC). Masters and Johnson developed this strictly physiological model of the traditional orgasm in the 1960s.[5]

I have added extended orgasm* and multiple orgasms* to this list and removed responses that would be difficult for you to determine. Also ask for your partner's observations, since in some instances it might be difficult for you to see how some of your physical reactions have altered.

Physiological Orgasm Changes

Below is a questionnaire that will help you identify the specific aspects of your arousal and climax that have changed. Write the number that best compares your physical changes prior to menopause to the present state of affairs. Then choose the letter that best describes your feelings regarding these changes. A—E

NO CHANGES - 1 - 2 - 3 - 4 - 5 - 6 - 7 - N/A - EXTREME CHANGES

FEEL BAD ABOUT YOUR CHANGES - A - B - C - D - E - F - E - FEEL GREAT

	CHANGES 1-7	FEELINGS A- E

Initial Stage – *Excitement Phase* –

	CHANGES 1-7	FEELINGS A-E
• Response occurs quickly	_____	_____
• Rapid heart rate	_____	_____
• Faster breathing	_____	_____
• Deeper breaths	_____	_____
• Nipples harden or become erect	_____	_____
• Fuller breasts	_____	_____
• Engorged pelvic region	_____	_____
• Upper body rash – sex flush	_____	_____
• Vaginal lubrication (amount and thickness)	_____	_____
• Engorged clitoris	_____	_____
• Engorged inner lips	_____	_____
• Increased muscle tension	_____	_____

CHANGES 1-7   FEELINGS A- E

Second Stage – *Plateau Phase* –

- Responses are slower and more intense   _____   _____
- Increasing intensity of phase one changes   _____   _____
- Stronger contractions of vaginal muscles   _____   _____
- More contractions of vaginal muscles   _____   _____
- More swelling (engorgement) in outer lips   _____   _____
- Clitoris hides under its hood   _____   _____

Third Stage - *Orgasmic Phase* –

- Brief period of time   _____   _____
- Involuntary vaginal muscle contractions   _____   _____
- Sex flush – rash increases   _____   _____
- Accelerated heart rate   _____   _____
- Accelerated breathing   _____   _____
- Foot muscles flex   _____   _____
- Release of sexual tension   _____   _____

Fourth Stage – *Resolution* –

- Return to unexcited phase   _____   _____
- Swelling subsides   _____   _____
- Contractions subside   _____   _____
- Muscles relax   _____   _____

Multiple orgasms   _____   _____

Extended orgasm*   _____   _____

Make a mental note of those that are similar to what you experienced prior to menopause (lower numbers) and compare which ones no longer hold true for you now (higher numbers).

Your responses will be helpful when discussing your traditional orgasm changes with your partner. You might need to make only a simple adjustment such as occasional use of vaginal moisturizer to supplement your lubricant and/or additional physical stimulation. (Refer to Chapter 6 for information on vaginal moisturizers and lubricants. The book's website resource section lists brands and ingredients.)

Some of the lack of responses mentioned above (e.g., lack of vaginal lubrication or engorgement in the pelvic region) could be associated with further complications and are oftentimes accompanied by pain. There are a number of symptoms that can produce genital pain during menopause, and most arise from one root cause: declining estrogen levels.

What If It's Painful?

Vulva/vaginal pain is a huge factor in short-circuiting your desire for sex and should be alleviated if you and your partner are considering vaginal intercourse or vaginal penetration with penis, finger(s), dildo, or another implement. In Chapter 5, you will be introduced to a range of issues that could be contributing to your discomfort with intercourse—indeed, some women even describe it as agony. If you as a couple refrain from vaginal penetration or live in a sexless marriage because of persistent vaginal pain or fear of incontinence, it is important to follow the detailed guidelines in Chapter 5 to regain and maintain your sexual health. Actually, the health of your pelvic region has a significant impact on your broader quality of life. Not only does the pelvic area affect your sexuality, it also supports the proper functioning of your lower urinary tract.

Vaginal and pelvic floor exercises to sustain sexual health, along with information pertaining to specialized treatments[6] for urogenital atrophy*, will also be covered in Chapter 5. These treatments could be game changers for women who have suffered pain and/or leakage of urine during and after intercourse.

Pain may have your partner defining your libido as low if you continually reject his advances without explanation. He needs to be aware that your anticipation of pain with penetration is shutting down your capacity to be aroused. This is your body's natural protection against further injury and pain. Combine your responses with the negative impact estrogen depletion may have on your arousal system and the situation becomes even more confusing when trying to sleuth out the initial cause(s) for your lack of desire.

To complicate matters further you might be finding it difficult to separate your feelings of arousal, response, sex drive, and sexual desire. You are not alone in confusing arousal, drive, and desire;[7] it often seems impossible to tease them apart since they are intertwined and each impacts the other. Yet it is of utmost importance to know the origin of your issue, so you can figure out the best approach to remedy or control the situation. Otherwise if left unresolved, it just might feel like sex has an expiration date.

Does Sex Have an Expiration Date?

Your definition of "having sex" will decide its expiration date. If you insist on the traditional style of vaginal intercourse with an erect penis, this might be an issue if your partner cannot get hard enough to enter you or stay hard long enough to enjoy it, and if ED medications either do not work or interfere with his medical problems. Your vagina might be too compromised from various medical or hormonal issues creating pain that makes intercourse unbearable. This could be a temporary situation or one that is too difficult to treat. So if vaginal intercourse is your definition of sex and you experience any of the above, then yes it might feel like your sex contract has expired.

But think about what sex actually means to you and what aspects are important for you to feel sexually alive. Orgasm is a marker for some people, and that might change to just cuddling and/or kissing if medical problems or medications makes this difficult for either or both partners. Take it one step further and don't give sex a meaning—give yourself the privilege to examine what it means to you every time you wish to express yourself sexually. This is an opportunity to create a new journey to finding your *Personal Path to Pleasure.*

By liberating "sex" from the confines of traditional sexual expression, you can decide to express yourself in ways that may not be usually considered acceptable, but certainly bring joy to some people. Taking a dominate or submissive role in the extreme side of sex, basking in the pleasure of strong sensations—this can satisfy some people's sexual needs.

I have spoken with women who take up a creative endeavor such as quilting, gardening, or painting as their libido wanes. This outlet feeds the part of their being that once was filled by sexuality. Please do not take this to mean you cannot enjoy simultaneously the physical act of sex and these creative outlets. But for some women this holds true. The one substitutes for the other. This need not happen if you don't want it to.

I suggest you take this opportunity to decide there is *no expiration date.* Give yourself permission to explore and create sensations that bring pleasure to you and your sex partner.

Misleading Labels

Understand how the "low libido" label could be obstructing your path to pleasure. Describing yourself as a woman with low libido or having been given that label by your partner might have led you to make assumptions about your sexual self that are incorrect and perhaps even harmful. Sometimes labels, especially inaccurate ones, can be problematic.

It is not unusual for me to hear a woman question the low libido status her partner has conferred on her. She forgets that his comment refers to his *feelings* about her lack of response and assumes she must actually have a low libido. An example by my clients:

> "…but you told me I had a low libido," she ranted. He protested, "I was trying to find a reason for feeling rejected. I was pissed at you when I shouted, 'You must have a low libido.'"

In this case, the woman confessed to me she was not feeling sexually satisfied. The combination of her partner's perfunctory stimulation and her lack of orgasm did not motivate her to be sexual. She had originally spent several years assuming her low libido was at fault and tried various ineffective remedies, instead of getting help to discover why her motivation had disappeared in the first place. Once the problem was identified, the couple learned to add more prolonged stimulation to their repertoire and incorporate activities that brought the wife to orgasm.

Women can potentially mislabel their libido level after reading sensationalistic sexuality articles published online or in glossy magazines. These stories often rely on misleading information from studies and surveys that have used a model of men's sexual response to compare with women's reported behaviors. These comparisons can be best dismissed with an analogy: Most women would be considered short if their heights were compared to those on a men's chart. If women and men and journalists have long had the wrong impression about human sexual response, so have sexologists over the years. Let me close with some background.

A Super Condensed History of the Human Sexual Response Cycle

Masters and Johnson developed the Human Sexual Response Cycle (HSRC) in 1966 while observing masturbation and intercourse in the laboratory. Their study focused solely on the physiology of orgasm:

excitement/arousal-plateau-orgasm-resolution

When the esteemed sex therapist and psychiatrist Dr. Helen Singer Kaplan realized her clients were experiencing desire issues, she included the stage *desire*, which she placed before arousal in her own variation of the HSRC, as follows:

desire-excitement/arousal-orgasm

This version of the model treats desire as an innate psychological drive, which includes both the sex drive and sexual desire as they are defined in this book.[8]

The inclusion and placement of the term *desire* led many researchers and psychologists to believe that desire was always necessary for arousal to occur. There are still medical professionals today that diagnose women as having low libidos if they do not correspond to Dr. Kaplan's 1979 model.

In the late 1980s Dr. Rosemary Basson, a psychiatrist at the University of British Columbia, interviewed hundreds of women. She noticed that for many women the path towards creating an interest in sex looked different from Dr. Kaplan's model. Here's Dr. Basson's Circular Sexual Response Cycle:

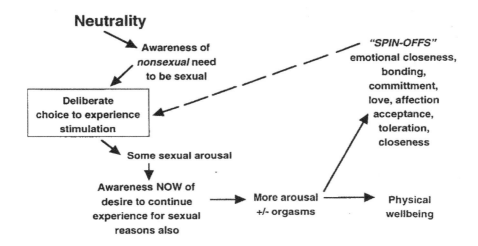

Dr. Basson concluded, "Women often begin sexual experiences feeling sexually neutral."[9]

The possibility of starting from "neutral" was a major revelation, giving women the hope that they don't have to feel desire for sex initially to become aroused.

At the beginning of this chapter, I introduced my *Sexual Pleasure Model.** It is a modified version of Dr. Basson's sexual response cycle, allowing for woman to not only have responsive desires, but also to start with sexual desire. The *Sexual Pleasure Model* displays sexual triggers as two categories: the unconscious and the conscious. This enables women to understand the differences and see where they need to be proactive as their innate trigger wanes.

It is the unconscious trigger women are referring to when like my client Tina they confess, "I woke up one morning and I realized my mojo was missing." Other women offer elaborate stories, but basically hidden in the narrative is a lack of interest in sex.

If in the past you didn't have to do anything special to feel an interest in having sex, and that desire is gone now, you too might feel like your libido disappeared. When hormones are raging, the innate sex drive functions mainly to evoke the need for sex. You might recognize the sex drive by other names, since it is sometimes referred to as an urge, instinct, lust, craving for sex, or perhaps you just feel "hot and horny," that unconscious, internal *physical* appetite to be sexual.

When hormones have tapered off and they are no longer heavily influencing the wanting of sex, women either experience what they refer to as a low libido, or they figure out how to activate their libido purposely. Being proactive and finding a stimulant that turns you on is how you can deliberately jump start your sexual desire.

In the early stages of your relationship, just the sight of your husband might have had you ready to jump in bed; he was your stimulant. Now you need to consciously spend more time creating your own desire and preparing for physically expressing your desires for each other. I suggest integrating external triggers into your preparation and sexplay repertoire—for example, reading sexually explicit/romantic writings and watching videos, using sex toys, experimenting with role-playing, fantasies, sexting, and so forth. These will help compensate for a declining sex drive when your unconscious sexual trigger has gone missing. Chapter 4 will give you creative suggestions on how to activate your libido.

When I explain to women the relationship between hormones and the unconscious sexual trigger and how they can supplement with conscious triggers to create the wanting of sex, I have frequently witnessed genuine—even instantaneous—insight, often followed by excitement, and occasionally bitterness, "Why didn't anyone ever tell me this was possible? Is it really this simple?" Sometimes all it takes is a bit of knowledge to understand your present situation and thus alter your *Personal Path to Pleasure.*

Recap:

The Sexual Pleasure Model

1. **Sexual Trigger**
    a. Unconscious –
        i. Sex drive
            1. Emotional (spontaneous erotic thoughts/fantasies)
            2. Physical (spontaneous physical sensations)
    b. Conscious
        i. External stimuli (fabricated fantasies, provocative situations, stimulation of body, use of explicit sex material)
        ii. Mental motivation (inner state of psyche)

2. **Sexual Arousal** - Interest in sex (physical)
3. **Sexual Desire** - Interest in sex (emotional)

    OR

2. **Sexual Desire** - Interest in sex (emotional)

3. **Sexual Arousal** - Interest in sex (physical)

4. **Sexual Satisfaction**
    a. Sexual pleasuring behaviors (sexplay, expanded sex, outercourse)
        i. Traditional orgasm
        ii. Non-orgasmic
    a. Spiritual/Sacred component (Neo-Tantra techniques)
        i. Energy orgasm
        ii. Non-orgasmic

In this chapter, I have introduced the *Sexual Pleasure Model* that explores the various interacting factors that lead to the wanting of sex. The misleading, catchall term "low libido" can mask a complicated menu of symptoms and causes—but most of these can be treated or counterbalanced.

Chapter 2 focuses on constructing a foundation of intimacy and trust with your partner. I pay special attention to the difference between secrecy and privacy and supply exercises to help enhance intimacy and your libido. The specific guidelines will assist you in establishing the essential ingredients necessary to ultimately create an *Authentic Sex Life*.

Chapter 1: Important Points

- One's *Personal Path to Pleasure* is an individualized approach to experiencing sexual pleasure and ultimately creating an *Authentic Sex Life*.
- The interplay of sexual desire, sex drive, and arousal produces the desire for sex. (For definitions of these concepts, refer to Glossary.) If there is a breakdown in any of these systems, it will have a negative impact on your interest in sex.
- Normal sexual functioning includes:
    1. Having the capacity to experience pleasure and sexual satisfaction with or without orgasm.
    2. Desiring or being receptive to sexual pleasure and satisfaction.
    3. Being physically capable of responding to stimulation without pain or discomfort.
    4. Being capable of experiencing (traditional) orgasm under suitable circumstances (the desire for orgasm, lack of distraction, effective stimulation, and so forth).
- Three medically attested symptoms of menopause are hot flashes, vaginal dryness, and the cessation of menses.
- The physiological model of the traditional orgasm, the Human Sexual Response Cycle (HSRC) from Masters and Johnson, includes four stages, starting with "excitement" and ending with "resolution."
- Dr. Kaplan's changed Masters and Johnson's model to a three-stage model that begins with sexual desire. This changed the original intent of the HSRC from a tool to measure physiological orgasm to a sexual pleasure/performance-based model. This modification to

the HSRC has skewed the results of many studies measuring women's desire for sex.

- Later studies by Dr. Basson have demonstrated that a woman doesn't have to feel desire for sex initially to have an enjoyable sexual experience. She can start from "neutral."

- Introduction of the *Sexual Pleasure Model,* which includes a Conscious and Unconscious Trigger phase.

- When your sex drive begins to wane, being proactive and making use of external triggers can help create an interest in sex.

2

OPTIMAL SEXUALITY, INTIMACY, COMMUNICATION, AND METACOMMUNICATION*

Components of Optimal Sexuality

We can learn much from long-term couples who are still enjoying their sexual lives together. A study was conducted with couples who had been in a relationship for 25 years or longer and who felt that they experience optimal sexuality.[1] The findings are extremely helpful for individuals who are interested in not only reviving their libido, but also continuing to remain sexually vibrant throughout their lifetime.

The following major characteristics of optimal sexuality were reported in this study:

- Being fully and completely *present* during sexual experiences
- A strong and intimate *connection* with one's sexual partner
- Deep sexual and erotic *intimacy* with a necessary sense of *trust* and deep mutual *respect, caring,* genuine *acceptance* and *admiration*
- Extraordinary *communication* and heightened *empathy*
- Being completely *authentic, uninhibited, transparent* and *genuinely oneself*
- Interpersonal *risk-taking* and *exploration* and the importance of *fun*
- Allowing oneself to be *vulnerable* to one's sexual partner and *surrendering* to the experience
- The experiences of transcendence and personal transformation, along with bliss, peace, and healing

The italicized elements are especially necessary for creating and maintaining a deep and meaningful relationship. Intimacy, communication, and metacommunication form the essential ingredients for creating optimal sexual experiences and an *Authentic Sex Life*.

The first step in creating your *Authentic Sex Life* is talking honestly with your partner. But talking frankly about your mutual sex life, which could have spanned decades, may not be easy. Being able to discuss your sexual needs as a couple, especially in relation to your sexual pattern, requires a comfortable dialogue. The guidelines in this chapter will help you enhance your intimacy and trust so you can speak your truth, which is of vital importance for achieving your goal. This is also a couple's issue, so make certain to hear your partner's desires and needs, even if you think you know them. While you may be familiar with his sexual style and amorous advances, you might not know what is motivating him.

It is not easy to summon an authentic voice within a society that supports the notion that women are sexual objects, easily turned on, ever ready and willing to be seduced by their partners. Virtually our entire media complex portrays women in passionate scenarios always welcoming of sexual overtures. Women are frequently depicted as ever-ready sex-bots, such as in ads for men's penile enhancing drugs (PEDs)*, or having orgasms with a head full of shampoo, or hair splayed out while fantasizing about a vibrating sex toy. However, these visuals are most likely not modeling your present feelings towards sexuality. If you compare yourself to these ads and, by contrast, believe your lack of sexual desire is not "normal," or at least low, you may find yourself steeped in guilt and shame.

If you are like many women and use sex as a barometer for your relationship status and no longer experience the yearning for sex with your partner, you might also feel as if you have fallen out of love. (Chapter 4 discusses sustaining an erotically charged relationship.) To further complicate matters, if your man has introduced PEDs into your sexual repertoire without discussion, it may have added a layer of anger to your humiliation.

The following composite scenario illustrates what could happen when a husband presents his wife with a gift of a hard cock, courtesy of Viagra. Tears welled up as Linda started to share the story of her husband Leo's "birthday surprise."

While he sang Happy Birthday, his present to me appeared as he pulled back the covers. A bright red ribbon surrounded his rock-hard cock. I couldn't hold back my shock at the sight. I just gasped—he hadn't had a hard cock in years. Leo misread my gaping mouth as desire and pulled me to him roughly. For a moment I felt as if I was being ravished, just like those bawdy scenes in a romance novel. I imagined myself a character in one of those books, but then without a word and barely any foreplay he entered me, or at least tried to. I screamed and pushed him away. It felt like I was being torn apart, horrible pain…. Then Leo mumbled something about how expensive the drug is and not wanting to waste it. This was definitely not romance, I was filled with tears of agony.

The scenario is not unusual, although details might differ (bows are rarely placed around a penis). During interviews for a New Zealand study,[2] men stated that their PED was intended as a gift to their wife. They couldn't imagine that she was being sexually satisfied without a hard penis in the picture. A similar study showed some wives complained that their husband's newly enhanced penis disrupted an otherwise satisfactory sex life that the couple had established without penile insertion. Other women noted severe pain upon attempt of intercourse, since their fragile vaginas were ill prepared to accommodate a rigid penis.[3]

Shortly after these small studies were published, I wrote a polemic criticizing Viagra for a class assignment, incorporating the findings of these studies together with anecdotes from couples I interviewed. For a lot of married men, erectile dysfunction (ED*) caused them to stop behaving sexually altogether, yet other couples expanded their sexual repertoire. The women most satisfied were those who had husbands willing to explore sexuality with a limp cock. Some even mentioned that their sex lives had improved since their husbands were no longer solely focused on genitalia. (See Chapter 6 on how to incorporate a flaccid cock into a mutually satisfying sex life.)

The menopausal women who were not interested in sex had found their husband's ED a blessing and became most upset when presented with a gift of hardness. Some of these women had never had to disclose their lack of desire, since their husband's ED and subsequent loss of interest had come first. When PEDs were introduced and subsequently a hard penis entered the scene, they had to confess that their desire had vanished prior to their husband's ED.

Perhaps you also have found it difficult to talk about sex with your partner and have been reluctant to discuss your libido concerns. At this stage you might be experiencing not only a sexless relationship (welcome or not), but something worse: one void of any touching. It is not unusual for couples to stop touching for fear one of them will mislead the other into thinking they want to go further.

If you have not been honest or comfortable discussing your sexual concerns with your partner, the guidelines in this chapter will help make this process easier. Be aware, however, that timing is a major consideration when planning to follow the recommendations with your partner. Whenever you or your spouse is angry, tired, drunk, or otherwise not at their best for listening or responding, postpone the exercises. And if one of you is constantly making excuses to avoid this next step, then consider consulting a therapist. Problems do not disappear spontaneously; they need your attention. Sometimes a third party is necessary to help negotiate difficult conversations, and perhaps nonsexual issues may be unearthed that are aggravating your problems. When you feel ready to proceed please know this is a process, and one that has the potential to change your perspective on your situation.

Intimacy*—And Privacy

Whether you decide to revive your libido or remain with your current state of sexual expression, I encourage you to develop a foundation of intimacy. This will help pave the way for a smooth transition to leading an *Authentic Sex Life*. Even if you feel your foundation is already strong, there may be areas that could use some attention. Yet being intimate raises the question of what can or should be discussed between partners. Both men and women have concerns about privacy and personal secrets. Often privacy and secrecy are subjects that get overlooked and are taken for granted, and this could lead to confusion and sometimes mistrust.

Please note that intimacy does not mean lack of privacy, which is quite different from keeping secrets. There are many gray areas in this arena, and within a relationship those grays are best identified and described so that each person knows the comfort zone of the other. Typical examples that clients have brought to my attention:

- Is it okay if I continue an email correspondence with a past flame as long as it remains platonic?
- Can I look up old "loves" on Facebook without telling my spouse?
- Do I have to disclose every time I masturbate?
- Can I watch porn without telling my spouse?

Let us define "privacy" as referring to areas a couple explicitly agrees not to discuss or share with each other, and "secrecy" as referring to what is not shared—and also has never been made the subject of any agreement between partners. Thus for the four examples above, a couple may agree to share details, or agree to NOT share details and keep this area explicitly private. But when there is no discussion at all, and no agreement one way or another, these four areas may remain "secret." Generally, privacy may be neutral or positive for a relationship, while secrets may be neutral or negative. Thus, I recommend that couples discuss such areas and develop their own guidelines or rules about disclosing details. However, discussing areas of privacy raises new challenges relating to "rules" for sharing (or not), and what can happen next.

If you agreed originally to disclose about an area and then change your mind without consulting with your partner, you put your relationship at risk by lying and breaking trust. When you hide any activities that affect the relationship, then that becomes a secret. People keep secrets for many reasons: fear of hurting their partner, fear of disapproval from them; fear of damaging their relationship, or fear from shame or guilt. You need to evaluate the reason for keeping your secrets. If it would harm your marriage or partner personally, then you will have to choose whether to disclose.

Think carefully about creating privacy rules or guidelines, and make certain they serve your relationship and are not just set up out of jealousy or spite. Make it a point to revisit them on a regular basis to see if the privacy statements are still contributing to your relationship.

The following composite story reveals how some couples learn about secrecy and privacy, and how desire discrepancy is sometimes at the foundation of their problem. Ellen and Rob had been married over twenty-five years and initially consulted with me because trust had become an issue. This is a condensed excerpt from our meetings. The parenthesis marks whether a behavior is secret or private.

Ellen: Rob was my first and has been my only. The problem arose when I became attracted to Ralph. I tried to hide it from Rob. (Ellen originally felt this was her private business, but later came to realize her need to keep this hidden meant she was keeping a secret.)

Rob: I saw our new friend Ralph with my wife at a café we never frequent. Of course, I thought they were having an affair. First, she lied. Upon leaving, she said she was meeting a girlfriend, and then the way they were looking at each other I thought for certain they were into each other. I was furious. Later when I asked her if she was cheating on me, she said definitely no, although she admitted she was attracted to him. I confronted Ellen because I thought she was keeping a secret and breaking our implied trust of a monogamous marriage.

Ellen: I lied about whom I was meeting. I didn't want to hurt Rob's feelings, since I never meet men alone (a secret to protect her husband's feelings and ultimately their relationship). I certainly didn't anticipate getting caught; it is why I picked a remote location to meet.

Rob: She could have just told me she was having coffee with our new friend Ralph. I couldn't imagine why she was sneaking behind my back, so I assumed she was having an affair.

Ellen: I decided to meet Ralph because he turned me on and that made me feel sexy- something I haven't felt in a long time. I didn't really want to do more than have coffee with him. Rob and I barely have sex anymore. I don't get turned on the way I used to. From what I've read this is common. But with Ralph, my body felt like it did the first time I met Rob; I was confused (private thoughts shared during our session together). I love my husband and would never cheat on him.

Rob: Must admit I've been thinking about cheating for some time now, but only thinking. I'm not getting any; you know what I mean. Well, hardly any. I was mainly pissed because I thought she was doing something I really wanted to do (initially private thoughts spoken for the first time in my presence). But I wouldn't really cheat, I'm too afraid if she found out she would want a divorce.

During our sessions together, it became apparent they were both interested in developing their *Authentic Sex Life* within their relationship. They agreed their previous commitment to monogamy was no longer working for them, but weren't certain how to proceed without hurting each other's feelings. We discussed various options for creating a *Conscious Coupling* that would honor their needs and keep the commitment to each other intact. Chapter 8 discusses *Conscious Coupling* in more detail and how secrets can be avoided with such an arrangement.

Erotic Connections

There are two well-known professionals in the field of marriage and sex therapy who have come to polar opposite conclusions regarding the life of an erotic connection. I have taken from each important elements that I believe are compatible and necessary to maintain this type of relationship.

Esther Perel, an esteemed marriage and sex therapist, believes that if you merge "as one," it is difficult for the chemistry of desire to be ignited.[4] Some of my clients describe this as being married to their roommate or living with a sibling, and as a result they have no interest in each other sexually. It may seem paradoxical but in order to sustain a sense of eroticism, there needs to be a sense of self, separate from the relationship. Appropriate parameters are necessary to maintain the self and keep passion sparking, but there is also a delicate balance necessary to maintaining self while simultaneously merging an emotional connection.

John Gottman, a leading authority on marriage, combined the results of the Normal Bar study[5] and his own research on more than 3,000 couples spanning over 4 decades, and identified 13 things all couples do to maintain an "amazing sex life."[6]

1. They say "I love you" every day and mean it.
2. They kiss one another passionately for no reason.
3. They give surprise romantic gifts.
4. They know what turns their partners on and off erotically.
5. They are physically affectionate, even in public.
6. They keep playing and having fun together.
7. They cuddle.
8. They make sex a priority, not the last item of a long to-do list.
9. They stay good friends.
10. They can talk comfortably about their sex life.
11. They have weekly dates.
12. They take romantic vacations.
13. They are mindful about turning toward. ("In short, they turn toward one another with love and affection to connect emotionally and physically.")[7]

The following story is a prime example of a couple being emotionally close while sustaining their erotic connection. My pedicurist Dorothy was starting to work on my feet, and so I became her captive audience. She began the pedicure ritual while simultaneously asking the typical small talk questions. When I told her the name of my forthcoming book, she bubbled with excitement and exclaimed, "Absolutely, yes, yes! Can I tell you my story?" Before I had the opportunity to speak, she started on what felt like an epic tale of true love. She and her husband Dan, 10 years her junior, met at a health club when she was 30. He worked there, and she worked out there.

> "I thought I would never get married," Dorothy said. "My Mom said I was too picky, and then I turned 30, over the hill I thought. I decided I better keep my body in shape if I had any chance of snagging a husband—and wouldn't you know- I met the man of my dreams at the fitness club. We've been together over 30 years, and we're still at it." She winked at me when she said that. Then she described in detail how they take care of each other's body daily, interchanging between washing each other's feet, sharing massages, bathing together, washing hair, giving each other facials, manicures and pedicures. Not only did she mention these acts of caring but described in detail how they were performed, all in a most sensual manner.

These acts of caring are often foreplay for what she described as "spectacular" sex, and she claimed it has always been good. Actually, she said it has gotten much better since they added the daily rituals of caring for each other's body. About 10 years into their marriage, sex began to feel bland, rather routine until they talked about what turned each other on, things that were not originally considered sexual. They keep adding to the list and realize it has saved their sex life.

They spend time not only acting out these rituals but they are also involved in finding new ways to keep healthy. They research together fitness exercises, recipes, lotions and potions, all to keep healthy. She confessed that she is not only doing this for herself, but she wants to keep his eye from wandering since she is 10 years older. I mentioned she certainly didn't look her age, and she added that she feels 20 years younger.

When their children were small, the kids were raised to be health conscious and were part of the "research" team to find new and better ways to stay healthy. She claimed the family is still close because of their shared interest in health.

She admitted that her husband is her best friend but they rarely take formal dates together, even though she has read in magazines they should. I believe their caring rituals are a wonderful substitute for dates, plus they are performed daily.

Dorothy admitted they even do the ritual when angry, the physical connection keeps them focused on each other and by the end the problem has usually been solved.

I'm convinced their couple/family focus on learning and doing things together regarding health has helped foster a close bond. But they have also learned to keep the "self" intact by exploring many of these issues separately and then coming together to share in their discoveries toward maintaining healthy bodies.

It has become apparent to me in listening to clients and various stories, along with input from my readings, that the lack of sustained erotic connections is one of the major issues in many sexless marriages and that the lack of sex is the outcome. Being able to create and nurture these connections forms the backbone for an optimal sexual relationship. Of course, all this is dependent upon your own sexually healthy body.

An approach termed Primal Intimacy can also help foster the qualities of an optimal sexual relationship by creating a safe and comfortable environment for discussions. (However, if you find you could use further assistance in creating a secure emotional bond, I suggest reading some communication books found on the book's website or consult with a relationship/family therapist.)

Primal Intimacy

Primal Intimacy is a nonverbal form of connection that lays down the foundation for healthy sexual intimacy. Below is a description from Stella Resnick, PhD, a well-known specialist in relationship and sexual enrichment.

> Words are not the mainstay of intimacy.... The most
> profoundly fulfilling intimacies for adults are those that are
> rooted in the body and involve the same primal needs we
> were born with...three basics for nurturing a more fully
> embodied, emotionally gratifying inner felt-sense of
> closeness: empathic touch, eye contact, and intimate
> kissing.... These primal pleasures provide the foundation for
> an attuned connection on which emotional, romantic, and
> sexual intimacies are built.[8]

The following daily rituals are the glue for many of my clients'
relationships—they are quite simple, yet extremely powerful. These
expressions of affection fulfill the primal needs described in Dr.
Resnick's intimacy thesis.[9] If you have been in a touchless marriage for
some time, start with holding hands and wait until that becomes a
comfortable feeling, and then move on to hugs. Performed regularly
with mutual consent, these rituals will ultimately become the
cornerstone for your healthy intimate relationship, helping to sustain
your erotic connection and ultimately an optimal sex life.

1. Hold hands while walking or in discussion, especially for a talk
   about a difficult subject. You can also hold hands while watching
   films or videos together. While in discussion, a hand or foot
   massage is a most relaxing behavior. (Caveat: There are some
   individuals who would find this directive distracting.)
2. Hugs, hugs, hugs, there can never be enough, at least one extended
   hug per day. Sometimes just a stroke or gentle clasping of the
   shoulder, arm, or back can send a very powerful nonverbal message
   of caring/love.
3. Eye contact during conversations. All right, not while driving or
   chopping the vegetables, but whenever feasible. Eye contact while
   expressing your feelings is exceedingly potent.
4. Lingering kisses, lasting approximately 10 seconds or longer
   depending upon your comfort. Kisses should be exchanged in the
   morning (before or after teeth are brushed, personal preference
   prevails) and when you meet again at the end of the day or prior to
   sleep. Of course if you wish to kiss more often, that is fine. A

wonderful good morning kiss can set the mood for a day of smiles perhaps even of a wanting…an implicit promise to be continued later.

You will become extremely attuned to these prolonged kisses and begin to notice differences depending upon your individual moods or how you are feeling towards each other. I would not suggest kisses as a consistent barometer of your relationship, but you will most certainly note any major changes, and minor ones might be noted unconsciously.

Mention your observations after kissing or save them for a later discussion, but only if you feel it would benefit your relationship. Especially if the kiss was spectacular, then by all means share. After all, you don't always want to focus only on the negative. Ignore most differences in kisses if you think there is little meaning behind your reflection. Please don't over analyze your kisses—enjoy, relish in the delight of sharing a deep physical connection.

While performing these behaviors, you could be exchanging tender signs of affection, or a wanting that expresses a deeper, more sexual longing, depending upon your intent. In the beginning, especially if you have had a touchless relationship, it is best to start with only one exercise. Wait until you sense that your intent has been read correctly. You don't want to feel that every sign of expression is a sign you or your partner wants sex. That might have been a past behavior or a misinterpretation, but look at these exercises as a fresh start. I encourage you to explore new styles of kissing, holding, gazing; it will allow you as a couple to change old patterns as a couple more easily.

For a detailed explanation of the chemical interactions and impact these affectionate actions have on intimacy with your partner, plus additional exercises, please follow the link on the book's website to Dr. Resnick's material. You will also find listings of studies that reinforce my suggestions about specific styles of contact.

Verbal Appreciation

Along with these physical expressions of affection, I recommend sharing your appreciation of your partner in words. Too often we take people for granted, especially the people closest to us, assuming that they know we love them. The expression of this love through one simple daily communication can help keep your relating-ship alive and well. (I like to refer to a relationship as a verb, always active.) Sex therapist Dr. Tammy Nelson noticed her clients reporting infidelity issues complained about lack of appreciation. As a healing and maintenance practice, she suggests that her clients offer daily appreciations to each other.

"Exchanging appreciations…can make your interactions more positive. Saying to one another, 'One thing I appreciate about you is…' sounds simple, but it can dramatically alter the power of negative communication in which you may find yourselves."[10]

Specifically, offer these appreciations for things that have meaning to you and your partner. Don't feel you are obligated and say something random just to fulfill this daily ritual; instead really focus on what your partner does that makes your life better, makes you smile, makes you feel good about being who you are, about being their partner. Make an effort to focus on sexuality, since it has become an issue. Don't ignore the white elephant in the room. For example, "I really appreciate that you give me such affectionate hugs, without expecting more." These should be honest and sincere statements; if there is any hint of sarcasm you will most likely create the opposite effect.

Checking In

Check in with each other on a regular basis—this will give you the opportunity to discuss matters that might otherwise be forgotten. This is also the perfect occasion to examine what is working and not working for you within your relationship.

Additional discussions might be helpful if one of you needs to rant or share a problem. In these situations, it is important that you express what is wanted in terms of feedback. Do you want to be heard with no suggestions, or would you like help solving the problem? Many an argument has started after a well-meaning partner tried to solve an issue that needed their ear, not their voice. By consistently checking in even when you don't have any gripes, you establish the foundation for open communication. The following samples are openers for check-in dialogues.

- Are you okay about…?
- How are you doing with…?
- Were you okay when I…?
- Did you feel all right when we…?

Talking about specific feelings, behaviors, and events may be more productive than talking about "our relationship." Here's a typical composite story. Dorothy and Randall have been married over 25 years and attribute their stable relationship to the check-ins they do on a monthly basis. They do not focus on this during one of their "date" nights (see story about my pedicurist, earlier in this chapter), but set aside a separate time to go over how each is feeling about certain situations that occurred in the past month.

One month after Randall retired he asked, "How are you coping with my being at home so much?" Dorothy responded with a positive statement (see next section in this chapter): "I really like that I can ask your advice, without having to disturb you at the office. But I'm not used to sharing my study when I'm trying to write. You ask me questions when I'm trying to concentrate on my work. I know you are learning the Internet, but with your constant interruptions I'm not getting enough work accomplished." Dorothy had been answering a lot of his questions quickly so Randall didn't realize he was bothering her.

In this instance they went back and forth brainstorming ideas. Ideally it would have been great if he wasn't in the space, but realistically the only place for his computer was in her office. They decided to rearrange the room so that they were not facing each other. Plus, Dorothy agreed to show Randall how to find a lot of his answers on the Internet himself. The ones he can't locate he saves for her to answer while he prepares lunch, or at the end of her writing day.

In the beginning, they both admitted it was difficult not reacting negatively to a critique. But as they continued to meet monthly, this became easier. They followed a pattern of thinking "out of the box" for a lot of the issues that were difficult to resolve and found that the laughter that often ensued helped clear the air for any negative feelings that arose. Their ability to overcome their initial reactions to critiques helped sustain an intimate relationship.

Criticisms Turned into Wishes

Giving critiques is a common method used to effect a change in action. Unfortunately, the message is usually carried in the form of blame, and the recipient normally responds defensively. This pattern thwarts any desired change and can even create animosity. Using the phrase "let's try… (specific behavior)" or *by reframing your critiques into wishes,* you avoid sounding like you are blaming and you allow the desired outcome to develop.

Dr. Harville Hendrix, a pastoral marriage and family counselor, developed the idea of substituting wishes for criticisms. He suggests sharing a genuine appreciation first, and then continuing by saying, "I have a request." This statement reframes your frustration without accusing your partner and setting him up for a defensive response. The intent of the "I have a request" is important, not the actual wording. Here is an example that Dr. Harville shared in one of his workshops.

> Harville's wife, Helen, is always running late. His "wish" is that she let him know when she is going to be late. Then he knows how to handle his time AND he also asks her that when she does finally arrive…to throw her arms around him and give him a big hug and a kiss!

The following story shows how criticism created a sexless marriage, but the couple's willingness to explore ended up expanding both their sex life and their marriage. Pat described the first thirty years of their marriage as content, despite being sexless for the last ten. Her husband, Jason, was her "first," and she faulted him for her lack of sexual pleasure throughout their marriage. Even their sexplay hadn't been enjoyable:

He didn't even know how to stroke my breasts. At first I told him he was making them hurt, but he just got angry and said he was trying. I finally gave up and told him not to touch them.

Pat confided they had not touched each other for the last ten years, but the real surprise came when she disclosed she always faked orgasms since she had never had one. She and Jason had remained physically monogamous until recently when Pat became attracted to another man. They had heated conversations about separation, even discussed divorcing, but decided their investment of thirty years and four children was not worth destroying over sex, which they hadn't even had in a decade. An agreement was finally met that allowed her to be sexually involved with this other man while remaining married.

I entered the picture when Pat's lover was interested in pleasing her, with lights on, and both naked. She was shocked by his request. She felt uncomfortable shedding the clothing that had camouflaged her years of neglect. But the real reason she walked into my office was that she had no idea what to tell him about pleasing her; she had never been sexually satisfied either through masturbation or with a partner. We worked first on body imagery, so she would feel comfortable in her exposed skin; then we focused on sexual pleasure. Pat had assumed men knew what buttons to push, how to stroke, what turned women on. I introduced the *Personal Path to Pleasure* concept discussed in Chapter 1, and how women need to be responsible for their own pleasure. She then followed the exercises in Chapter 3, where she learned what areas of her body were sensitive, what types of touches she enjoyed, and how to pleasure herself. Not only did she orgasm for the first time, but the body she so had hated for all its blemishes of aging she began to embrace.

The next step ensured that she communicated her desires effectively to her lover. Pat practiced how to create "wishes" instead of critiques by asking for what she wanted. "Your fingertips on my thighs really turn me on, and I'd also love our eyes to connect while you're stroking me."

Pat eventually took all she learned and brought it home. She continues to see me, but now we are focusing on how she can enjoy herself and give pleasure to the two men in her life. Pat and Jason are enjoying a renewed intimacy, while she continues her relationship with her lover. She is on her path to discovering her *Authentic Sexual Self.*

Adding another person to your relationship is certainly not necessary for you to learn about her body. However, in this case it was the catalyst for change. Often people do not change without first being forced out of their comfort zone.

The Focus of Your Communication: Reviving Your Dormant Libido

In talking to your partner about sex, keep in mind your reasons for doing so. The key element to reviving your dormant libido is to explore the benefits you receive, or have received and/or want to receive from behaving sexually. What do you ultimately gain from being sexually active? Intimacy, comfort, touch, spiritual high, orgasm, tension release, love (to give and receive) are just a few reasons women mention in reference to creating sexual pleasure. Examining the incentives you marked in Chapter 1's questionnaire ("Why Would YOU Want Sex?") can help you explore the benefits obtained from expressing yourself sexually.

Focusing on how you personally benefit from behaving sexually is an important element to establishing a healthy libido. If you have sex *only* to please your partner, having sex again will build resentment and make any sexplay feel like a chore. Ultimately, the imbalance of pleasure will have you choosing not to respond to his overtures. Now, this does not preclude being generous and offering to satisfy your partner's sexual needs periodically even when you are not in the mood. The key word is "periodically." But when this happens all the time, then animosity often appears.

Your relationship will benefit if you initiate sex occasionally, even if this is the furthest thing from your mind. Remember: you do not have to feel aroused at the beginning in order to enjoy sex later, once things have gotten started. (see Chapter 1.) Many women confess that when they initiate sex they eventually receive great enjoyment from their husband's pleasure, plus they experience an enhanced sense of connection and closeness. Under these circumstances, it is not unusual for you to become aroused while responding to your partner's enjoyment; this is known as the arousal feedback loop*. I suggest giving yourself permission to initiate, and see if your partner's pleasure turns you on.

I would not recommend creating times only for his pleasure on a regular basis, unless you also have similar sessions where only you are being pleasured.

Exception—you can decide to establish a relationship where your participation is focused only on your partner's pleasure, and you remain asexual. This *must* be mutually acceptable; do not allow yourself to be coerced into this type of arrangement out of guilt.

I found out quite by accident how I get turned on by my partner's sexual responses, even without a sex drive. We had been watching *Tom Jones*, a classic movie from the early 60s with one of my favorite food scenes, when I realized it didn't turn me on as it had in the past. But that evening, I decided to have fun and duplicate the scene with the chicken my partner had prepared. His imitation of the scene had us both in a state of laughter when I realized his lustful response turned me on. We continued our laughter as we climbed the stairs to our bedroom.

When appropriate I suggest to clients the following exercise since it appears quite simple yet can produce powerful results. While being held in their partner's arms they are to masturbate, giving them the opportunity to hyper-focus on their own pleasure with no expectation of having to return the favor. Then afterwards if they both desire or on a different occasion, they are to switch positions. My clients all have different experiences when they follow these instructions, but there is one common feeling that occurs. It seems to heighten the affection and intimacy towards their partner. Unless you are totally averse to this style of pleasure, I suggest you both try it. Perhaps you will experience a similar response as my clients, an enhancement of affection and intimacy toward each other.

Self-pleasure can also be used as a trigger to get turned on. My new client Dave had originally requested if I would see him alone, since his wife Fran was not interested in having sex nor was she interested in going with him. Her constant rejection of his sexual overtures left him extremely frustrated. I suggested he try the following homework assignment: masturbate in front of his wife. He was to ask her just to observe, with no physical interaction between them. Dave was extremely skeptical with my request. Since his physical advances had been refused, he couldn't imagine how his solo sex would inspire her to want sex with him. But he was willing to give it a try, since none of his efforts to turn her on had worked.

Dave came to his next session with Fran by his side. She smiled sheepishly while listening to him recount the assignment results.

> Fran agreed to watch me as long as I didn't insist she touch me or get in bed with me. I was naked on top of the bed, and as I began to rub my penis I recall she sat quietly with an extremely stern face. She was in the rocking chair that she had placed on the other side of the room, as if she couldn't get far enough away from me. Then I began to make noises of pleasure as you had suggested, but this was not easy for me. I kind of had to exaggerate a bit, since I wasn't used to making sounds except when I have orgasms. At one point I glanced over at Fran and our eyes met and we both smiled. I noticed her hands were under the skirt she wore, playing with herself. The rest is a bit of a blur.

> Fran chimed in immediately, "But I remember quite clearly." She spoke to him directly. "Your sounds, you never made them before and it really turned me on." Then she looked at me. "I asked him to slow down, and we both came within minutes of each other. I immediately hopped into bed and we clutched at each other, crying. I have never felt so close to Dave."

These are just a few examples of how to get turned on. Chapter 4 will delve further into expanding your erotic connection with your partner. If you plan to revive your libido, be aware that it requires your commitment to create time together for intimate sexual pleasure. I suggest you initially set aside at minimum a session once a week for several months. This is not the time to discuss in-laws, financial matters, check-ins, or anything that would distract you from creating sexual pleasure. Call it whatever you want: a date, a rendezvous, homework, but don't leave it to chance or wait until one of you feels in the mood. You both can create your own pet term for these times, like "playdate," or "loving time." The date actually starts before you become physically intimate. You could spend a leisurely day walking the woods, picnicking, turning each other on from a distance, but your ultimate goal will be sexual pleasure later (with or without orgasm or intercourse). Having sex is not a natural act for humans; especially at this stage of your life, it takes conscious planning. Of course, if the mood strikes you both at other times—enjoy!

Specific Guidelines to Alleviate Low Libido, with Communication Tips

The crucial step to overcoming lack of interest is *willingness* to become aroused, even if you are not initially interested in sex. (See Chapter 1.) You might find this comment strange, perhaps even offensive. But if you are willing to accept that your old style of preparing yourself for sex is no longer working, or if you never feel any internal sex drive, then you might be willing to try a variation that has the strong potential to spark your erotic energy.

At midlife, women need to take responsibility for getting in the mood, even if desire doesn't arise as spontaneously as it used to. (Chapters 4 offers a variety of suggestions.)

> A fifty-six-year-old colleague told me that for her, "getting older means *deciding* to have a sex life, instead of being *driven* to it." The good news is that getting in the mood is a choice that begins in your mind![11]

With the knowledge that you do not have to wait for internal erotic cues to propel you to act sexually, you can allow yourself to enjoy discovering new approaches to creating sexual desire.

Some of the suggestions for establishing a new sexual voice might seem awkward at first, especially if you don't have any internal drive to act sexually. Try to keep an open mind and an open heart, and be willing to allow yourself time to respond. In *Naked at Our Age*, author Joan Price quotes sex therapist Dr. Diana Wiley suggestions:

> Most women have to be physically stimulated to feel desire. So women, who think they need to be in the mood to have sex, might in fact need to have sex to be in the mood! In other words, *just do it!*[12]

This might sound like an outrageous statement, but changing your perspective and viewing the desire for sex more as a **decision-making process** than an inherent urge allows you more control over your body. I know my body rarely has the urge to go to the gym; it is usually the last thing on my mind if my day is full. And even when I've made the decision to work out, it takes a while until I'm actually involved and committed to exercising. But then I feel most alive and invigorated.

In deciding to have sex, here's a "best way" to proceed without either of you getting offended. Agree on a gesture or phrase that means your partner wants to express his love for you physically. This should be one that you can comfortably respond to with a *just do it* attitude, or decline while setting a future date. Optimally, these signals should come after a period of expressed erotic connection.

Women have shared with me specific signs indicating their partners wanted to have sex. They range from extremely loving to quite crude, but they were all effective in getting the point across. It is a matter of finding one or more that work for you as a couple, where there are no misunderstandings and no offense is taken. Examples of signals mentioned by these women:

- He says "Let's go upstairs." (…and it is not even bedtime.)
- I feel his hardness as he clutches me from behind. (Usually while washing dishes or standing at my desk.)
- He caresses my nape ever so gently and looks me in the eye.
- A hug with his hardness between us, no words necessary.
- He looks at me with longing eyes and says, "I want you."
- He gives my hand an extra special squeeze after we've been holding hands a while.

Some of these signals are quite subtle, but what matters is you both know what they mean. I suggest creating new signals if the ones in your past didn't feel comfortable. You can also decide to agree on new ones to complement your new *Authentic Sex Life.*

At some point you might want to extend the same invitation, or perhaps sometimes use a different gesture that you both agree means, "I only want to cuddle" or "I'm willing to…." This gives you the opportunity to be proactive within your limits. Below are some examples to express your love and entice your partner to behave sexually, but as stated earlier they should be the culmination of an erotic connection.

- Some of the above samples can work with roles reversed.
- Lean up against his thigh and grind a bit.
- Grab the inside of his thigh, especially when he is still wearing pants.
- Look deeply into his eyes and bite your lower lip gently.
- Suck gently on one of his fingers while looking him in the eyes.

Whether you use any of these signals or create your own, they must reflect a personalized expression of your true feelings. If your partner is offended or they do not create the desired effect, then continue to discover ones that work. As a couple, you could have a lot of fun experimenting. Trying gestures, observing effects, exaggerating a bit, and at the end falling into bed with great laughter. You might need to remind yourself sex is fun, especially if it hasn't been lately or never was. If you like a purely verbal signal, you can come up with amusing designations for sexplay, such as "Let's dance in bed" or "I'd love to taste you tonight." Many couples have developed their own private slang for genitals and sexual acts that allows them to avoid impersonal, formal terms like *penis, vagina* and *intercourse.*[13]

How some couples deal with snuggling in bed is similar to the suggestion of "just do(ing) it." Paul C. Rosenblatt interviewed couples for his book, *Two in a Bed*, where he examined "the social system of couple bed sharing." Rosenblatt noted,

> Respecting a partner's desire not to make contact (in bed) was often not a problem. But if the lack of contact went on night after night, difficulties might arise. Perhaps to head off difficulties, some people would force themselves to snuggle even if not in the mood. One could say that, in a sense, they were not respecting

their own needs, but sometimes they could find that the snuggling put them in the mood for snuggling.

Replacing the concept of snuggling with a sexually focused behavior, one could easily see how a sexual encounter would follow. One of Rosenblatt's interviewee stated,

> Sometimes I'm not in the mood for cuddling, and if he tries to snuggle I'm like, "Eh, leave me alone...." And vice versa. Sometimes he just doesn't feel like snuggling, and so I respect that, I know how it feels.... Other times when I can tell he really wants to snuggle and I'm not in the mood, I just try not to make an issue out of it, and then eventually whatever it is that's bugging me that makes me not want to snuggle kind of fades away.[14]

The word to focus on is "bugging," since there are times the circumstances might not feel exactly right to have a sexual encounter. But if you wait for the stars to align and all the noises to dissipate, there might never be a right time.

Speaking of bed manners, snuggling can often lead to sex, and perhaps individuals do not want to offer a snuggle thinking they would be leading their partner to expect much more. This also holds true for the couple that no longer touches, even out of bed. Debby Herbenick, PhD offers a suggestion that might prevent or release you from a touchless relationship:

> Embrace sensual pleasures: How might you experience pleasure with your partner in ways that don't involve sex? Could you be more affectionate with kisses, hugs, or pats on the back? If he or she truly does spring into sex every time you offer affection, saying (gently, and with a smile) that, "Sometimes I just want to kiss" is one way to be clear about your intentions.[15]

Here's my client Angelica's response to the homework assignment I had suggested:

> I took your recommendation and changed my mind-set. Even though I had absolutely no desire to hug, let alone have sex, I went with the flow. At first I felt nothing, but then I decided—just this once. Giving myself permission to enjoy it only once seemed to work. Well, of course we have enjoyed sex a few times since my last appointment [via Skype], but I always start from the premise—just this once.

This attitude keeps you in the moment, rather than jumping ahead and thinking, "I'd best not give in—he'll want to do this more often." Offer alternatives if you are truly not interested in sex for the moment: "I would really like to have sex, but I'm busy at the moment. Would you wait a few hours/till tomorrow/etc.?" Be specific so that your partner doesn't feel like he's being brushed off. This is especially helpful if you are feeling coerced into acting sexually and you acquiesce in hopes that he will leave you alone. Have sex on your terms unless you have made the decision that sexual expression will not be part of your relationship.

Communication Regarding Sexual Behaviors

Some of the most difficult, and for many, awkward conversations to have are about sexual behaviors. Discussions regarding sexual pleasure can happen during sexplay or outside the bedroom. Try both ways and see which one works best for both of you. I'm including some questions that will help you get started in your exploration of body pleasure with your partner. Customize the questions by filling in the blanks indicated by ....

The following exercise is most effective if you both answer these questions. I suggest sharing your answers in print if talking is awkward at first. Sometimes a letter/email/text message discussing the answers are a great way to open up verbally in the future.

1. I would like to show my love for you like I have in the past. What can I do so we have sex (again) or (more often)?
2. What (did) or (do) you like most about our (past sex life) or (sex life)?
3. For me, one of the best times we had sex was when … It was great because….
4. When you do…you put me in the mood for sex.
5. What are some ways I (put) or (have put) you in the mood for sex?
6. It sometimes (always) takes me a while to get turned on in bed these days. Would you do…to help me?
7. What can I do to help you get turned on in bed?
8. I wish we could do…in bed, it would make me feel closer to you.
9. What do you wish we could do in bed to make you feel closer to me?
10. When we are (were) in bed and you did … it really turned me off.
11. What do I do to turn you off in bed?
12. Before we are even in bed, when you do…it turns me off to having sex with you, because ….
13. Before we are even in bed, what do I do to turn you off to having sex with me?
14. I love it when you…in bed.
15. What are some things you really enjoy that I do in bed?
16. I wish we did…more often in bed.
17. What do you wish we did more often in bed?

My clients had the following ideas for starting the conversation and asking some of the above questions:

- Nancy's husband surprised her one evening as he gently slid behind her in the bathtub. Initially she felt like he had intruded on her private space but then she decided to use this time to her advantage. She asked for a back scratch, since she was wedged between his legs and he could reach her easily. Then he proceeded to kiss the nape of her neck, "I cooed with pleasure, he had never done that before." The conversation began slowly, as he asked what else would make her feel that way. It drifted from bathtub to bed in dialogue only, without ever moving. They started to turn each other on by asking what turned each other on, and sometimes showing by example. The bathtub turned into a bed of pleasure.

- Kay and her husband John were living in a sexless marriage when they started consulting me regarding her self-diagnosed low libido. It became apparent quickly that her libido was fine; it was her husband's sexual skills she felt were lacking and she didn't know how to get him to change. Since they had been together over 25 years, Kay thought it impossible to confront him with her needs. So she just went without, and then her desire for sex disappeared. I suggested she start talking to him on the walks they took after dinner. These walks were usually in silence, not for any particular reason other than they felt little need for verbal interactions. One evening she took his hand as they were walking and blurted out she had been speaking with a sexologist. Her hand and words startled John since they had not been having sex for some time now and barely touched anymore. Kay continued by explaining that she really wanted to have more sex but felt she didn't know how to please him, other than by their usual method of making love. And then she squeezed his hand since she wanted him to know this was difficult for her to express—"I love you but having sex for me became boring so I guess I just didn't feel in the mood and then I lost my desire for sex. But ever since Linda (her good friend and also a client of mine) has been talking to me, I've decided I want it back and want it to be different and exciting." Her desire to please him was the plan to start the conversation and as they continued their walks it quickly became a back and forth dialogue that included her pleasure. They talked about everything from technique to role-play to fantasy. The walks eventually became part of their sexplay to turn each other on.

The following questions are taken from Reid Mihalko's[16] suggestions. He is known among "sexperts" as the Sex Communicator Guru. One or more of the questions are best asked while in bed, at the appropriate time.

1. "Do you like when I…"
2. "I like when you…"
3. "Will you…?"
4. "How does this feel?"

5. "Do you want me to...?"

6. "Do you want to...?"

7. "Is there anything you want to try?"

8. "Show me what you like."

9. "Do you want to go further?"

10. "Do you want to stop?"

11. "Can I...?"

12. "Does this feel good?"

13. "Are you happy?"

14. "Are you comfortable?"

15. "Are you having a good time?"

16. "Is this good for you?"

I suggest you use the above questions to create a basic foundation of what feels good and what doesn't. If you are experiencing issues, it is your responsibility to inform your partner of any health changes. Or you can alter your responses on a whim. Don't wait for the questions to be asked if you are uncomfortable or suffering. Take turns with your partner focusing on one or two questions at a time, and linger on the ones that challenge you individually and as a couple. These are the ones that could effect the greatest changes.

Ray and April's time spent with me is a great example of how these questions can positively affect a diminishing sex life. April had been experiencing vaginal pain during intercourse, and so her gynecologist recommended she use vaginal moisturizer to remedy her dryness. She had further questions regarding her orgasms and sexplay, but she felt her doctor was uncomfortable addressing these issues. A friend mentioned my specialty, and I suggested we meet without her husband initially so she could learn how to self-trigger her desire for sex.

Then we focused on her tenuous orgasms and worsening arthritis, which made it difficult to move comfortably in bed. This is when we invited her husband to our sessions.

We discussed how the above questions could be used to set a baseline for comfort and pleasure, and then I advised the couple to continue monitoring any changes in how sensations were perceived. At first they asked each other a lot of questions during sexplay, but when it began to feel intrusive and they felt surer of themselves, they devised nonverbal signals. These cues answered many of the questions even before they were uttered.

April realized that by modulating her sounds of pleasure, Ray didn't have to ask her constantly if something felt good or bad. Also, her breathing style automatically signaled a desire to stop, or for him to continue creating sensations of pleasure. They both acknowledged that her vocal sounds were contagious, "This was the first time I heard Nancy make noises during sex, except for her little whimpering when she was having an orgasm. It really turned me on and I found myself directing her hands with my sounds and heavy breathing. Nancy interjected, "That's funny, I started to feel more turned on listening to you." They both laughed and noted how the directive to use questions led to a nonverbal bed language.

Now let's take another look at Linda and Leo from the beginning of the chapter. How might Linda have handled her situation differently if she had learned better communication skills? Perhaps something like this:

Leo: Here's your big surprise! (Pulls back covers while singing Happy Birthday; he has an erection with a ribbon tied around it.)

Linda: Wow! That's really beautiful and big.

Leo: C'mere, honey! (He gives her a quick rough kiss while trying to enter her.)

Linda: Whoa, tiger! (Smiles at him and takes his cock in her hand.) You must feel wonderful about this but I need to take this slow. It has been a long time since you were inside me and I'm not sure this is going to work, but I'm willing to try if you'll help me.

Leo: I paid a lot for this pill—what do you mean it might not work?

Linda: Well, my body has changed. I'm tighter inside and not so juicy. I've been talking with friends and reading articles, which has made me a bit scared.

Leo: Oh Linda, I bought this for you (as he shows her the PED bottle), thinking you were missing my hard cock. And of course I wanted to be inside you again, I miss how you feel.

Linda: But I've really enjoyed the way we have been making love since you have gotten soft- real slow and tender with no intercourse. Maybe we can do both.

(This might work depending upon the health of Linda's vaginal canal. If her pH is off or her muscles inflexible, it will be a painful experience. She will need to learn techniques on how to work with her internal and external physical challenges. These will be discussed in detail in Chapter 5.)

Now here's another alternative scenario, this time assuming that the couple have *both* learned communication skills. So Leo's approach is quite different.

Leo: I know your birthday is in a few weeks and I've been thinking about a present for you. I really would like to give you this (he hands her a blue pill and she looks a bit bewildered)—it's a med that will help make my cock hard. I'm sure you would like that, I know I would, I miss your soft insides.

Linda: Oh Leo, this is not easy to say, but the last time we had sex it really hurt. So I was actually glad you couldn't get hard anymore, since I didn't have to have this awkward talk. And now I really like our long evenings of making out. I thought you did too.

Leo: I do, but I thought you missed being penetrated. Must admit I also miss being inside you.

Linda: I've been reading a lot about some products that could help get rid of my pain. I'll ask my gynecologist and see what she suggests. (Linda was extremely dry and her vagina had shrunken and become inflexible. Lube was not going to be enough to solve this issue. Her doctor advised Linda stretch her vagina using dilators for several weeks prior to attempting intercourse. She also suggested Linda use a vaginal moisturizer when she is not having intercourse along with a lubricant prior to penetration.)

Evening of birthday:

Leo: Happy Birthday sweetheart! (Leo is lying under covers covered with rose petals; Linda had mentioned a while back how she found them most romantic. He pulls back the covers to unveil his beribboned hard-on, while Linda is wearing another present: lingerie he had left on the bed earlier that day with a love note anticipating their evening together. The nightstand is covered with lubes, feathers, and other accouterments to entice.)

Linda: (After placing a long deep kiss on Leo's lips she murmurs.) I love your luscious kisses. (He turns her over gently onto her back and proceeds to feather whip her skin and then the evening progresses very slowly, giving Linda a chance to become aroused and prepare for intercourse.)

This scenario differs because of the degree of intimate knowledge shared. In the first scenario, the lack of information has Leo believing Linda would be delighted with a hard cock as a gift. This assumption has led him to misread her reaction and hence his aggressive sexual behavior. He is let down and also pissed because not only did he spend a lot of money on this gift, but he has been left to deal with a hard cock on his own.

In the second scenario Linda gets to practice her newly acquired communication skills. She is still dealing with the same situation but she is not responding with a defensive stance. Linda feels empowered because she is communicating more effectively, allowing herself to share her feelings honestly and willing to listen to her partner's desires.

In the final scenario Leo and Linda have learned to communicate their needs and be honest about their desires. They have become familiar with each other's concerns and wishes prior to the birthday evening. Neither is defensive, and both are respectful and willing to listen to the other without being defensive or causing guilt. The birthday is more likely to go smoothly and if there are any difficulties they will probably not blame the other. If vaginal penetration is still a problem for Linda she can suggest using outercourse for them both to receive sexual pleasure. (See Chapter 6 for outercourse techniques.)

The backbone of this chapter has been communication. You have been provided with various exercises to enhance intimacy and trust with your partner plus gain an understanding of your libido. Guidelines and tools to assist you in establishing an *Authentic Sex Life* have also been offered.

Chapter 3 concentrates on activities for exploring your new *Personal Path to Pleasure*. Exercises will focus on expanding your erogenous zones along with guidelines for understanding your menopausal body.

Chapter 2: Important Points

- The major characteristics of optimal sexuality.
- The media depicts women as sexual objects, always ready to respond sexually.
- Women's sexuality issues are often steeped in guilt and shame.
- Equating having sex with relationship status can cause you to feel you have fallen out of love with your partner.
- Penile enhancing drugs can further complicate a woman's perception of her sexual self.
- Lack of communication regarding your libido concerns can lead to a sexless or touchless marriage.
- Do not try to resume sexual activity just to please your partner.

- Create a solid intimacy foundation to develop an *Authentic Sex Life*, which means to honor how one feels about their sexuality and consciously act on it.
- Create privacy rules to avoid secrets.
- Set appropriate parameters to maintain the self and keep passion sparking.
- Emotional intimacy is a prerequisite for optimal sexuality.
- Primal intimacy is a nonverbal connection that forms the foundation for a healthy sexual relationship.
- Primal intimacy incorporates daily rituals for a healthy intimate relationship, and can include:
  a. Holding hands
  b. Hugs
  c. Eye contact
  d. Lingering kisses
- Exchange daily verbal appreciations that have personal meaning.
- Check in regularly to examine the relationship.
- Set guidelines for feedback.
- Reframe critiques into wishes.
- A key to reviving your dormant libido is exploring the benefits you receive from behaving sexually.
- Initiate sex occasionally.
- Explore pleasuring each other.
- Set specific times for sexual pleasure.
- Another key to overcoming lack of interest in sex is willingness to become aroused.
- Create signals that indicate whenever either of you is interested in behaving sexually.
- Take responsibility for getting yourself in the mood. (Chapter 4 offers information about how to turn yourself on.)
- Desire for sex is a decision-making process rather than a spontaneous one.
- Offer an alternative time if you have no interest in sex at the moment.
- Tell your partner about sexual behaviors that give you sexual pleasure.

3

SELF-DISCOVERY: EXPLORING YOUR NEW BODY

The Double Standard Doubles Your Trouble

My female clients who are interested in reviving their old style of spontaneous sex are initially disheartened when they learn that it probably won't happen. However, they do leave our sessions assured they won't miss their old approach, since the new one will allow them more control over their pleasure. I explain my *Sexual Pleasure Model* and how it differs from older sexual response cycles with the inclusion of the trigger phase as two categories—the unconscious and the conscious. Once they understand how they have to be proactive to create conscious triggers and that these stimuli differ for each woman, discovering their *Personal Path to Pleasure* follows.

This chapter consists of exercises that might seem awkward at first, especially if you have never examined or touched yourself, but these exercises are an important aspect of creating your new *Personal Path to Pleasure.* This is a powerful experience, made so by a society that has fostered a "good girls don't—don't touch themselves / enjoy sex / want sex" culture. I commonly hear older women refer to masturbation and sex in terms of good girl versus bad girl: "I was taught only bad girls touch down there... In my day we called bad girls (those that enjoyed having sex) nymphomaniacs." Society's voice is ever pervasive with the longstanding double standard on what is sexually acceptable for women.

Even men suffer from this double standard—for example, if they dare just want to be held instead of playing the stereotypical ever-horny aggressor. As for women, they are not expected or encouraged to enjoy sex, be aggressive, ask for what they want. This is slowly changing, but older women have had those voices playing in their heads for decades and many can't imagine some of the advice of the inner voices not being true.

I recall an impromptu discussion with women wanting to know how to jump-start their libido. One of many suggestions I offered was to read or view explicit sex materials. A few women gasped, "…but I'm a feminist!" Since feminism is all about equal rights for women, I couldn't understand their outburst. It became clear that they assumed all sex videos demeaned women and could not even imagine that this type of material turns on some women. But they also had never been exposed to "couples oriented" and "feminist porn," produced by women and designed by women to appeal to women.

Many women still believe it is only men that get turned on by explicit material even though studies and surveys have certainly proved this to be false.[1] But if your inner guide equates porn with men and you can't imagine ever looking at it yourself, you will probably not allow yourself to be psychologically turned on by the viewing. Some women have overcome their squeamishness by viewing instructional videos that can also be quite provocative while simultaneously presenting sex education material.[2] Chapter 4 gives detailed instructions on how and why to use erotic material as a couple, even if the woman herself does not get turned on by it.

Older women are especially embarrassed by their lack of information or inaccurate information regarding sexuality—when they were young, "good girls" didn't learn about sex either. Now mature, they believe others assume they know it all, so they rarely seek out answers for fear of being judged as stupid or as "dirty old ladies" at this stage of their lives. Some women do have the courage to ask questions, but they are often met with silence, disapproval, or hedging from untrained or uncomfortable health care providers. This sends a message that older women are not expected to act sexually.

When doctors fail to include sexual evaluations or ask about sexual matters during routine medical examinations, it implies that the medical world believes that sex belongs to the young and healthy. This situation reinforces society's notion that sexuality is equated with youth, which is the model for beauty and for many the necessary precursor to sexual desire. Entire industries have evolved based on aging women feeling inadequate and needing to conform to a youthful image.

Health care professionals also avoid discussing the impact of newly diagnosed medical conditions upon a patient's sexuality. Tears streamed forth as Debra described the response when she asked her doctor about the possible effect that her cancer treatment could have on her sexuality. Her young female doctor dismissed her questions and said, "You should be grateful you're alive!" My client was made to feel ashamed of her desire for sexual health and, thankfully, found her way to me. Have you had chemotherapy or other medications that interfere with expressing yourself sexually? Please access the resource section on the book's website for links to specific sites dealing with depression, cancer, other illnesses and disabilities, and their impact on sexuality.

I encourage you to do some of the following exercises with your spouse. Examples suggest specific wording, but please reword and replace with language you commonly use when speaking with your partner.

Sleuthing Out Your Shame

The following messages impact women's sexuality (oftentimes subconsciously) and their decision to either abandon or revive their *Personal Path to Pleasure*. I encourage you to explore your inner self-talk, and uncover your beliefs regarding sexuality. Otherwise, the voices that dwell in your head, similar to the good girl versus bad girl mantras, will hinder your process of sexual self-discovery.

Your inner voices get their power from various sources, such as your religious upbringing, family values, social taboos, cultural prohibitions, and past sexual experiences (especially if they have been abusive ones).

<u>Exercise 1:</u> One or more of these mantras could be influencing your unconscious thoughts and ultimately your decision to explore your sexuality. Review the list and note which ones give you an "aha!" reaction:

- Thou shalt not... (Finish the sentence with a sex-negative word/phrase you recall hearing from the pulpit.)
- Shame on you! You're bad! (Words you might have heard when getting caught in a sexually compromising position, such as playing doctor, masturbating, examining yourself in the mirror, etc.)
- Don't talk about sex with your partner; just do *it*.
- You don't need to talk about sex—it just comes naturally.
- You're too old for sex. Old people having sex? Ewww!
- Go on a diet.
- That's dirty, don't do that!
- Sex toys are perverted.
- Vibrators are addictive.
- Your vagina smells bad.

Which of the above phrases do you relate to? Many often translate into self-imposed restrictions on sexuality, such as:

- I don't deserve pleasure
- I'm not worthy of ...
- I'm too old...
- He can't possibly like my... (my wrinkled skin, my scars, my extra weight, my hair, my...)
- I can't touch myself, it's a sin.
- I can't ask him to...

Do any of these restrictions sound familiar? Your head might be filled with some negative thoughts like these, but like many women you probably never acknowledged or questioned them. Feelings of shame tend to render us silent, and if ignored will obstruct the process of developing your *Authentic Sex Life*. The silence translates your mantras into actions that affect how you behave sexually.

Your inner voice might speak loudly, or it could be so pervasive that you don't even notice it exists.

Some of the following behaviors or lack of behaviors might be ones you can relate to easily. These are directly affected by your belief system, which influences your judgment of sexual expression and self-esteem.

Exercise 2: Read through the list below and find the behaviors that apply to you. Then ask yourself: Why does... (behavior) make you feel uncomfortable? Find a time in your past where this behavior was comfortable and see if you can figure out when and why it changed. If it was never comfortable, when did you get the message this behavior was unacceptable? If it brings up traumatic memories, find a therapist who will help you with these issues.

- You are no longer expressing yourself sexually, although you are not experiencing any physical or psychological discomfort.
- You insist on lights out when being physically intimate.
- You would never wear provocative clothing such as lingerie.
- You dislike when your partner touches the extra flesh on your body.
- You never expose your naked body.
- You never masturbate.
- You forego having an orgasm because it takes too long.
- You don't like to give or receive oral sex.
- You wish your partner spent more time arousing you.
- You wish the sex act went faster so you can get it over with.
- You won't use a sex toy.
- You won't make sounds of pleasure.
- You won't speak erotically or use "dirty" words during sexplay.
- You won't use a vibrator.
- You never experiment sexually.
- You never look at your naked body.
- You won't allow your partner to look at your body.
- You never look at your partner's naked body.

- You have never seen your genitalia.
- You would never watch or allow your partner to watch an explicit/erotic video to get turned on.
- You would never read or allow your partner to read erotica/explicit material to get turned on.
- You would never read a "sex manual."

I encourage you to personalize this list by adding or subtracting items that make you feel uncomfortable. It is not necessary to partake in any of these behaviors, but to help you find your *Authentic Sex Life*, I suggest you explore your feelings and beliefs related to them. You might be pleasantly surprised at the outcome, especially if at some point in the process you invite your partner to participate.

Several years ago, I co-hosted a sexuality and aging workshop. We used a fishbowl arrangement: the inner circle of men spoke first, and the outer circle of women listened. Then they reversed positions, and the women spoke while the men listened. The two groups shared experiences dealing with body changes and how these impacted their sexuality. Afterwards the circles blended and a discussion ensued. It became apparent for both women and men that a lot of assumptions had been made regarding self-image. Women's concerns regarding their weight gain turned out to be largely unfounded, since the majority of men confessed they preferred their wives' mature softness to their hard or overly thin bodies as younger women. Janice, a pleasantly plump woman shrieked in anger, "Why didn't you tell me you would have preferred me fat? I wouldn't have spent so much time dieting." Her husband, Richard, calmly defended himself, "I told you many times when you were younger, and in one of your plumper stages. I loved the way you felt then and do now." Janice then responded less accusingly, "Guess I didn't believe you, since I noticed you always looking at thinner women. You still do." "You're right," Richard admitted sheepishly, "I like the way they look. But you're my wife, and I prefer your softness."

By the end of the workshop I concluded that some men did enjoy looking at thin women in passing, in videos, or in illustrations, but preferred softer ones by their side in life and in bed. (Exercises on how you relate to your body, fat or thin, and discovering the connection with pleasure will be explored later in this chapter.)

The following story will demonstrate the impact that cultural upbringing, misinformation, and assumptions can have on sexual behaviors. A colleague relayed a story about her client Mary, who finally had found the courage to consult with a therapist because she had been married to Ned for over 20 years and complained of no orgasms. Dr. Gray asked for more details, and her client said that she could not orgasm when she was having sex with her husband. When Mary was asked if she could orgasm when she masturbated, she responded emphatically, "Every time." The therapist suggested that she pleasure herself in the presence of Ned, and Mary gasped. "I would be too embarrassed to do that!"

After several sessions, it was determined that Mary's embarrassment stemmed from several causes: the glossy magazines professing, "It is the husband's job to make his wife orgasm," and the fear of her partner's response when she expressed her climax with contorted face and loud moans. Mary was convinced only women in porn movies made those kinds of noises. During her therapy sessions, she learned that she was ultimately responsible for her sexual satisfaction and pleasure and that it was common for women to express their sexual pleasure in sounds and words. Mary then approached Ned and asked how he would feel if she made those kinds of noises during sex. He admitted, "That would really turn me on." She couldn't believe his answer but found out the truth when she challenged herself and shared her orgasm with him for the first time. Her moans of pleasure created an arousal loop that fed her own desire and arousal also, as well as his.

If you can relate to any part of this anecdote, Chapter 4 will help you to develop a sexual intimacy that allows for comfort in sharing with your partner. But first it is important to start the process of locating the origin of your inner voices and acknowledge their role in your behavior. Otherwise you will fall into your old habits, and they will block you from accepting pleasure.

If you have been sexually abused, <u>do not</u> proceed any further. Skip to the next section about abuse, following these questions.

Over time it is not unusual to develop patterns of responses to calm your inner guide, avoiding situations that would awaken and intensify the voices in your head. The process to transform those habitual reactions is an equally lengthy one, but one that can proceed in stages. You do not have to work on every issue before you see changes. Prioritize the ones you feel need your attention the most and start with those first.

<u>Exercise 3:</u> Notice the actions that trigger your bad feelings, sometimes just a gut feeling. Your responses noted from the list will help evoke situational memories. Focus on the inner voices that stopped you from acting with more abandon, ones that spoke loudly when you tried to step out of your normal style and left you feeling bad or where you couldn't even imagine trying to change. Allow yourself time to answer the questions below in detail. For each action where you felt bad or responded negatively recall a specific situation, and include how your partner reacted and how you responded to him.

Once you have discovered the experience that produced your shame or discomfort, then write a brief account about it, including what your inner voice was telling you. If you feel comfortable sharing your responses with your partner or good friend, do so, but ask them initially only to listen and be a witness to the tale surrounding your responses. After telling or writing the story from your perspective, ask yourself how you would respond if your inner voice were not dictating your actions. This is where you have the opportunity to change your behavior:

1. Would you feel comfortable dismissing your inner voice?
2. If not, what do you fear would happen if that voice were no longer in your head?
3. What would that say about you as a person?
4. How would your actions be different if your inner voice gave you permission to change?... If your inner voice forgave you for past sexual behaviors that you regret?
5. What does your inner voice foresee as the consequences of the forbidden activity? Do you think these consequences are likely?

If after following these self-therapy questions you still feel there are issues holding you back from experiencing sexual pleasure and developing your *Authentic Sex Life*, I suggest you consult with a therapist.

If You've Experienced Abuse

Women with issues stemming from sexual abuse should not follow the instructions on self-therapy. It is best to consult with a therapist who can help you handle the intense feelings that often arise during analysis. The process of confrontation, that is, examining your beliefs towards this impactful event, will help you heal from the traumatic experience.

Verbal and cognitive behavioral therapy, EMDR (eye movement desensitization and reprocessing) and Model Mugging (full-force, self-defense program with padded assailant) have all been successful treatments for past sexual traumas and PTSD (post-traumatic stress disorder). Your goal is to find the one(s) that works best for you.

A psychologist treating Elaine for PTSD episodes, which interfered with her daily life, suggested she consult with me. Recently she had become anorgasmic, and the doctor felt my expertise in sexual behaviors and libido would benefit Elaine in restoring her orgasmic response. She had seen many therapists previously in hopes of alleviating her PTSD. After 20+ years, nothing seemed to help and now we concluded that it was affecting her ability to orgasm. While Elaine was my client, Model Mugging was being introduced at the local YWCA to teach women self-defense. I suggested she attend since she carried a well-founded fear of being attacked. Recently there had been several rapes reported in the area where she lived.

This program has given women the opportunity to learn techniques to defend themselves against attackers. At one of our last sessions Elaine was smiling—she finally was orgasmic. I wish I could have taken full credit by attributing her success to one of my homework assignments, but she told me that it was her Model Mugging course that effected the change. While fending off a mock assault during a classroom session, she had envisioned attacking her father to resist his sexual abuse. Elaine was empowered by the mere emotional simulation of "killing" her abusing father in her imagination. This allowed her to confront her real father in person and resolve her issues of rage, remorse, and shame, enabling Elaine to lead a less burdened life.

It is important that your partner be part of the process of your dealing with past negative sexual experiences. He need not be present for all your sessions with the therapist, but at some point he must be brought in to understand and support you in your efforts to heal. (A listing of therapists and treatments can be found on the book's website.)

Head to Toe: Thoughts and Memories

Now the fun begins, as long as you trust in the process—the process of developing your *Personal Path to Pleasure.* In order to find out what turns you on, it is essential that you are comfortable living in your body.

The next step towards developing your *Personal Path to Pleasure* begins with knowing your body: how it looks stripped of its artificial layers of clothing and how it feels to your touch. It was not unusual for my interviewees to confess they had never touched their breasts erotically. They didn't know if their nipples turned them on, or in some instances how to give themselves an orgasm by breast stimulation.

Viewing your body as a holistic entity is an integral aspect of reclaiming your sexual pleasure. When you examine your body and don't like a particular aspect or aging alteration, how you feel about it gets communicated to your partner. In bed you might show your self-consciousness by changing positions, hiding yourself under covers or demanding lights off. You might not even be aware of your feelings regarding specific parts of your body, but you've most likely developed unconscious habits to compensate for your emotional body discomfort. For example, you might not feel comfortable having your partner give you oral sex because you think you smell bad. Perhaps you recalled that one time he complained you smelled like fish, and you found out you had bacteria vaginitis, abbreviated as BV. (The vaginal pH* level is higher after menopause, that is, greater than 4.5, predisposing your vagina to bacterial infections.) Smelling yourself first will give you the opportunity to know whether you need a treatment for BV. Place a clean finger in your vagina and smell it. Yuck!? Well, you want your partner to place his tongue there (if you do), and he only says "yuck" when it smells bad. Best to visit your gynecologist for medication if you smell like fish or have an extremely unpleasant order. If you itch and/or have an unusual discharge, this might also be a sign of an infection. (A pH of greater than 4.5 in the absence of vaginitis symptoms is a good indicator of menopause or in some instances atrophic vaginitis.) Chapter 5 details the relationship between the pH factor and vaginal health.

I often hear women complain, "Well he should know what I like, he's done it enough"—meaning to have sex. Even if your partner did know what you liked in the past, things have changed and it is not always a bad thing as you will see. But unless you know what pleases you, you can't expect him to be aware of your personal pleasure zones. Women's bodies have some of their highly sensitive areas hidden, making it a challenge not only for your partner to find them, but you as well. The following exercise will help you in accepting its imperfections and limitations.

Exercise 4: The initial process of exploring your body is to get it emotionally comfortable and cleansed. You can do this simultaneously in the shower or bath by rubbing your soapy hands over your entire exterior body. Please, no bubble baths or soap near your vaginal opening because the chemicals in these products are harmful to your sensitive vaginal wall. Some women find the addition of music and candles calming for their soul. Maybe this is your normal cleansing routine, but this time focus on how your body feels to your touch.

After you dry off, stand in front of a full-length mirror and look at your body. You can use a handheld mirror to view your back. Make certain the temperature is comfortable for you to stand naked for a period of time. Best to scan your body systematically starting with your head and working towards the bottom of your body or vice-versa. This method can help avoid bypassing sections of your body. Do this exercise initially alone, but speak your random thoughts and comments aloud. I suspect this will feel awkward but saying the words so you can hear them and giving feedback verbally will produce a different outcome compared to doing it silently.

Some questions to ask yourself while referring to specific parts of your body that stand out for you:

- How do I feel about my…? (specific body part)
- What person does this body part remind me of?
- Would I prefer this part of my body to look differently?
- I would like it to look like….
- If it were possible to alter this body part, would I do it?
- If it is not possible or too expensive, how can I change my attitude about how it looks?
- What can I do to change this aspect of my body?

An example I heard at a workshop, "My hair reminds me of my mother. When I pass a mirror, I see my mother's face, her darkened hair color and hairdo. I miss her, but I wish my hair looked different. I never really liked the way she colored her hair. I think I will stop dyeing my hair. I'm going for the gray!"

Although I'm advising you to do this exercise naked, the exercise can also be done clothed and it can even be an interesting session if done with close friends. Lots of laughs and sometimes tears may erupt when the exercise triggers memories of relatives, injuries, and other things associated with your body parts and scars.

Once I performed this exercise in front of a small intimate group. After discussing various parts of my body systematically from head to toe, I sat down only to realize later I had left out my genitalia. I was most upset, but realized my genital health was compromised at the time and my brain decided it wanted no part of it.

The second part of this exercise concentrates on touch. Find a comfortable position sitting or lying down in a warm space, since it is easier to touch your body if you are entirely disrobed. Again, start at the head or feet and work systematically to the other end. You can apply a moisturizer to your skin while you hyper-focus on how your body feels to your touch and the sensations your touch produces. What parts of your body really enjoy being stimulated and which parts are you rushing through, trying to avoid? (Include your outer genitals, keeping in mind that the next part of the exercise addresses the outer and inner genitalia in more detail.)

Best to do this part of the exercise alone at first; in the future, have your partner witness the assignment and share your thoughts with him. Be honest with yourself and your partner but don't be hurtful, especially if you haven't been candid in the past. As you are touching your genitals, if appropriate, you could say, e.g., "I felt the need to fake an orgasm because I wanted you to stop pounding.... It hurt, and I was too afraid to admit this to you.... I was too embarrassed to confess I've never had an orgasm." When you divulge secrets such as these, you open your heart, make yourself vulnerable, and allow intimacy to flow.

While your partner is present during this exercise, as you touch a specific part of your body relate it to his touches. Always start with a positive first, e.g., "I really like the way you pinch my nipples." If you would like his actions to change, be most specific, "I would prefer you wait 'till I'm about to orgasm then play hard with my nipples, but I really enjoy light strokes with your tongue first."

If you get to a part of your body that he has never stimulated, but you realize it now feels good, mention this. If you are not certain how you would like to have this integrated into your sexplay, ask him to experiment. Sexplay is all about the sensual dance of sex. When you're in flow it is hard to tell who is leading and who is following unless you specifically set the parameters to create this distinction.

After you have viewed and touched your external body parts, you may decide to immediately continue or come back to the next exercise at a later time.

Tiptoe Through the Two Lips

The third part of Exercise 4 is learning about your genitalia, a crucial step to creating sexual pleasure. Have you ever looked at yourself in a mirror, specifically between your legs? Does an "eek" factor appear when you even think of looking—down there? If you are serious about your pleasure, then take the challenge. Find a hand-held or small propped mirror, since you are about to explore the wondrous folds/layers of your vulva and vagina.

You might have performed this exercise previously in your life, but if your desire for sex has changed most likely this area of your body looks different. Consider that you probably look at your face at least daily while washing or brushing your teeth, why not take another look between your legs?

Set aside a period of time to get acquainted with your external and hidden parts. Make certain your hands are washed and your nails are trimmed or at least have no ragged edges. Then familiarize yourself with the anatomical illustrations found on the book's website.

As in the earlier self-exploration, start by doing this exercise alone, then invite your partner to join. Place him wherever you are most comfortable and he is also able to view what you are seeing. He can sit by your side, facing you, or you can sit between his legs as long as his position doesn't hinder the process and you are both able to view the mirror.

Create a private warm area to view your crotch comfortably. Place a towel under your butt, just in case juices start to flow. Some women lean up against the headboard of their bed or on the floor leaning on the wall. You can also lie down with your head bolstered on a tall pillow, and in all positions with knees bent and spread comfortably, feet flat to the surface.

Expose your crotch to the reflection of your mirror as you view the various parts that make up your genitals from top to bottom: the clitoral hood—pulling it back to expose the tip of your clitoris, your inner and outer labia—stretching your lower lips wide to view the opening of your vagina, and tilting your pelvis slightly upwards to see your anus.

Once you have viewed your genitals in detail, the next step is to locate the erogenous zones hidden both within and on the surface. Lubricate a clean finger, making certain your nail is smooth, and gently explore sensations around and inside your vulva and vagina. (A list of safe commercial and homemade lubricants will be on the book's website.) Now that you know where everything is located from the diagram on the website, you can close your eyes and let your fingers do the walking. Long fingernails can be problematic if you explore inside your vagina; you must be extra gentle with the vaginal walls, especially if they have been thinned out from lack of estrogen. However, stroking your lubricated clitoris with the tips of your nails ever so lightly can be a most divine sensation.

All the touching and stroking can be performed using sex toys/aids (an extensive list with reviews can be found on the book's website). However, for these exercises I suggest you use your fingers so as to give yourself the opportunity to actually know how your body feels, not just making it feel good.

Ahhhh! The elusive G-spot, a most contentious area that even sexologists cannot agree actually exists. I don't think you need a scientist or research study to tell you what feels good and how to respond. I propose that if you find an area that is exceptionally wonderful inside and along the vaginal canal, call it whatever you want, and enjoy the sensations. These are spots/zones you probably want to share with your sex partner. When you find an area that is extremely pleasurable, play with it, try varying your strokes, your intensity, your speed. Sometimes pressing firmly can enhance a feeling, other times quite the opposite. Think feather light touches, dancing on the surface of your skin with your fingertips.

Stimulating your G spot is best tried after you feel somewhat aroused. Finding the hidden G-spot is usually the most difficult part of the exercise—it doesn't actually reside on the surface of the vagina. It is an area that gets felt through the vagina and is easier for post-menopausal women to discover, since their estrogen is waning. With the decline of estrogen, the walls of the vagina become thinner, making access a simpler procedure.

Lying on your back, sitting up, or squatting, insert one or two well lubricated fingers into your vagina and bend them slightly in the direction of your bellybutton. You can then feel for a hard spongy textured "walnut" that varies in size from a dime to a quarter. It is located anywhere from ¼" – 2" along the top wall of the vagina. If you have felt this spot when you were younger, you might have noticed a change in size and location as you have aged. This is normal; gravity has a way of drawing things down, and the vaginal canal shortens.

Apply pressure to this zone. If you feel like you need to pee, congratulations! You have found it. This sensation will probably subside in about 30 seconds or less, but continue stroking while pressing firmly on this nut-shaped area. Make certain to maintain a lubricated area while stroking, since thinning vaginal walls can easily tear.

The towel you laid out earlier might become useful now, since occasionally women squirt or dribble fluid while having their G-spot stimulated. Many times, it is an odorless liquid—occasionally, it might be urine. If you feel no sensation or if it hurts, try changing techniques. If you feel nothing, then this may not be a sensitive area for you. (Some women prefer locating their G-spot initially while in a shower stall or tub, in case they pass urine or ejaculate.)

Ménage à Moi

Most couples masturbate, together or solo; strictly for pleasure, as a sexual exploration, or to relieve an itch. It is not uncommon for women to confess it is the only way they can orgasm. Only about 50% of women report they can orgasm solely through intercourse without direct clitoral stimulation by hand or object. These women may have a clitoris located closer to the vaginal opening, thus enabling penetration to stimulate the clitoris more directly. With most women, penetration stimulates the clitoris indirectly, through that organ's internal structure. I suggest that women who want to orgasm during penetration either self-stimulate or have their partner stimulate them during intercourse. Some women feel the woman-on-top position gives them the opportunity to do this comfortably. Other women prefer "doggie style" so they have a free hand to stimulate their clitoris: balancing on one hand while kneeling on the bed, leaning over a pillow or kneeling beside the bed, resting the upper body on the bed.

Exercise 5: Some women only masturbate when they feel the need to relieve that sexual itch of arousal, usually a tingling sensation from the clitoris or a heavy feeling from vaginal swelling. Others enjoy masturbating specifically to induce orgasms, alone or during sexplay with their partner. It is one of the first sexual behaviors women have little interest engaging in if they no longer feel the desire for sexual pleasure. It is also one of the first pleasures I suggest you engage in in order to explore your body and revive your interest in sex.

Bring yourself to orgasm by your favorite method of self-stimulation. Then refer to the Physiological Orgasm Changes chart in Chapter 1, and note any changes that have occurred while you were abstaining from sexual gratification. If you are uncomfortable with this exercise, ask yourself why? The answer might not be initially evident, but give it a guess. Often the first thought is the right one.

Sit with it awhile; but if it definitely feels wrong, guess again until your answer sparks a memory.

Knowing the beliefs you hold regarding masturbation is important for understanding what is hindering the enjoyment of your self-pleasuring. This might also be the source underlying your present discomfort with sharing your body. I suggest seeking professional counseling if this exercise has proved too challenging or has brought up history that is difficult to deal with. There may be deeper issues keeping you from enjoying this process.

Some of you might relate to Jasmine, who was raised in a Christian family that believed masturbation was a sin. She found this out when she was caught rubbing up against a pillow at a young age. Jasmine was not only reprimanded but also used as an example to her siblings. The humiliation this caused kept her from masturbating and ultimately knowing very little about how to be pleasured. My esteemed friend and colleague Reverend Dr. Beverly Dale has noted, "Masturbation is never mentioned in the Bible; it is only through interpretation that people believe it is forbidden."[3]

In the second part of this exercise, I propose naming or renaming your genitalia to acknowledge the relationship you have created with your newly explored body parts. Some of the names I have heard in masturbation workshops and individual sessions are Curly, Nancy, Cutie, V, Lovely, etc. You could have lots of fun developing various nicknames with your partner, which can be used interchangeably depending upon your moods. Anatomical terms are politically correct, but please leave them at the door of your bedroom. There is little that is politically correct about sexual expression, and an intimate setting demands special consideration. Friendly slang can work too, like "pussy," "muff," or "pleasure canal" among the many possibilities to describe your "private bits." (You and your husband might want to make up a special way to refer to his penis, too: "Steve Junior" using your husband's name, "magic wand" or "cock" can start you brainstorming for more words.) Any word is fine, as long as you are both in agreement and the word makes you feel good about your genitals.

Whole Body Erogenous Zones

You explored the classic highly sensitive areas of the genitalia in the section, "Tiptoe Through the Two Lips." But an extremely important aspect of the *Personal Path to Pleasure* is discovering erogenous zones that are located throughout your body. The number of nerve endings decreases as skin ages, along with decreased blood flow. As a result, your skin registers sensation of pressure and temperature differently. The areas that might have turned you on when you were younger may no longer hold appeal, and perhaps some spots that once were considered off limits are craving to be touched. Initially you might feel disheartened by these changes. It could also be one of the major reasons you are unable to become aroused and ultimately feel no desire for sex.

Exercise 6: In locating your highly erogenized zones, take the time to figure out what areas turn you on and share them with your partner. Give yourself the opportunity to explore your body as if you are doing so for the first time—Buddhists would call this, "...with fresh eyes." If you attend to your body anticipating your typical responses, you will keep yourself from exploring areas that have never been touched or had their tactile senses altered. Keep an open mind and allow yourself to experience the pleasures of unexpected sensations. You are certainly welcome to revisit your genitalia and see if this time your "fresh eyes" reveal different sensations.

Exploring Your Sensual Body

The exploration and heightening of sensations is where you get to discover what turns your skin into a layer of pleasure, and a trigger that has the potential to send your body into ecstasy.

Palms, fingertips, and nails are the body parts most commonly used to create intense sensations, but individuals with long hair can also use their mane as they would a long-bristled brush. The tip of the tongue and different intensities of air emitted on the outbreath can be used to "massage" the skin, producing heightened sensation of pleasure. These are just a few examples of how to trigger the body to turn on. I encourage you to explore what sensations feel best.

Chapter 6 has an expanded section on off-label use of products found at hardware, kitchen, and toys shops, supermarkets, and other unlikely stores. Various household items can serve dual purposes, initially as intended when produced and the other as an item to create sexual pleasure. Bedroom paraphernalia can be created from a variety of items if you look through the aisles of these shops with a creative mind, one focused on creating sexual pleasure and sensual delight.

I had great delight once walking through the aisles of a gigantic home store while rummaging for prospective sex toy materials. My partner and I flirted and giggled while we whispered exactly how we intended to use these products. We couldn't wait to get home and try our new pincers, ropes, and other prospective sex toy hardware gadgets.

Creating Erogenous Zones

By drawing on the brain's ability to change (known as neuroplasticity*), your entire body has the capacity to feel heightened sensations. I developed a method using traditional orgasms as a mechanism to create associative changes. When you have a genital orgasm while simultaneously stimulating another part of your body, your brain has the ability to draw a connection between the two areas. For example, you can vigorously massage your scalp while stimulating your clitoris. You can even have your partner play with your scalp while you are in orgasm, setting up an association that could have you becoming extremely aroused or even climaxing every time he touches your scalp in the same manner.

And you are thinking, "What happens if he touches my scalp in public? Oh, no, never!" Remember, you are in control of your responses; his touch might feel wonderful, but ultimately it is your emotional response that will decide whether to convert it to an orgasm. Also, this process also takes time. I cannot give you specific numbers, but persevere and it probably will work. And there are always exceptions when it works the first time, or not at all. Nonetheless, the exercise includes an orgasm, so simply trying can give you much enjoyment.

Taboo Discovery

Let me encourage you to discover the pleasures of an area of your body that is integrally connected to your pelvic muscles, contracts during orgasm, is highly charged with blood vessels and nerve endings, and has the capacity to create exquisite sensations, yet is shrouded in social taboo—the anus. Anal eroticism is not an expression usually heard in conversation, unless you happen to be speaking with a sexologist. (Note: The anus is the opening; the rectum is the canal leading away from the anus up into the body and connecting to the lower intestine.)

Please take the courage to get acquainted with this area of your body; it has the potential to bring you much pleasure. You may decide this is not a sensation that could ever translate to pleasure: your mind is thinking dirty = feces. But if you cleanse yourself thoroughly with mild soap and water or intimate wipes beforehand, dislodging any matter that you think might have gotten caught up in the tiny hairs surrounding your anus, there will be no fecal matter left in the anal zone. One caveat: do not place any object or part of anatomy into your anus and then put that object or part immediately afterwards into your vagina. If you want to switch to vaginal stimulation, use a different toy or wash the object or body part thoroughly. Or cover the finger or object with a condom or disposable glove for anal stimulation, and discard the protective items before using the object or body part elsewhere. Tiny bacteria can get caught on objects and be transmitted to your vagina. The other direction—moving an object or body part from vagina to anus—is fine.

Also, be most careful with the shape of the object you insert into the anus. It must have a flared base or sizeable handle large enough to remain outside the body. Unlike the vagina, which is effectively a closed cavern fully surrounded by tissue inside the pelvis, the anus leads to the passageway of the lower intestine. An object inserted in the anus can get lost and sucked up into the lower intestine, only to make you wait most embarrassingly in the emergency room for its removal.

If you have long fingernails, take caution to stroke even more gently than you would with your finger. Trace the pucker of your anus and notice the sensations; they will most likely be quite strong. They might not translate to pleasure in your mind yet, but allow yourself to feel the difference between this muscle and the areas surrounding it.

Feeling particularly adventurous? Lubricate your fingers and massage the area around your pucker and then slowly encircle your anus. You can carefully enter with the pad of one of your fingers. *Do not* poke with the tip of your finger. The likelihood is you will remain tight and it will not feel good. At any point you experience physical pain, stop, this is all about pleasure. And if one finger feels good and the sphincter muscle is relaxed you can move the finger around, moving it in and out a bit, add another finger if you wish or just stop altogether.

With you partner present, make certain he is aware of how you are feeling about this area of your body. You have several choices on how to proceed. If he has tried to enter in the past and it was painful, but he is noticing how much pleasure you are receiving from this area, then you two might want to have a discussion about how you would like to proceed with integrating this area into your sexplay.

Any fingers going into the anus should be washed thoroughly afterwards. Another option is to use a disposable glove on that hand.

You might decide you would like his tongue to match your finger, a most exquisite feeling for some women, or just have him use his finger. (Prior to anal tongue pleasuring, place lubricant around the entrance to the anus and a bit inside, then cover the area with plastic wrap.) Jack Morin, PhD, the author of *Anal Pleasure and Health*, asks people who are interested in exploring their anus to "make one fundamental commitment to yourself: From now on, I will do everything within my power to protect my anus from any pain or discomfort whatsoever." His book along with others listed on the book's website offer excellent advice to create a pleasurable anal experience.

If anal exploration felt good, but you are definitely not interested in taking it any further, I suggest that you allow yourself the opportunity to change your mind. As with anything in life, sometimes it is all about timing. In the height of sexplay, a finger might wander, but instead of reacting automatically with disgust and taking yourself out of the moment of pleasure, stay in flow and see where the play leads you. If you are not interested in being adventurous, then move away from the finger or gently remove his finger. No need to linger with negative thoughts.

Women have confided they have sometimes ejaculated with anal intercourse. This is possible if the penis is hitting the G-spot via the inner wall of the rectum. Some women can orgasm from the feeling of a full anal canal and the position of the penis, which may stimulate the pair of internal legs ("crura"; the singular is "crus") of the clitoris.

Orgasms: Current, Past, Future

Exploring a "new" sexually responsive body and discovering your *Personal Path to Pleasure* can be a most rewarding experience. It is essential to note that your path to creating orgasms will continuously fluctuate as you age and not to expect that any particular recommended technique will necessarily work. Please, don't let your partner, friends, or magazine articles convince you otherwise. Your *Personal Path to Pleasure* is unique and it is yours. The traditional Human Sexual Response Cycle might be the physiological model your body follows to produce orgasms, but your personal sexual script* is what influences your fantasies and how you create and perceive pleasure. Your script is unique, and is an integral aspect of how your mind translates physical arousal to an emotional response of pleasure. It is in the mind where orgasms are manifested and have the potential of becoming most extraordinary. However, if you are following a traditional female sexual script filled with shame, your perceptions and beliefs might keep you from experiencing sexual pleasure and the type of sex that has one wanting for more.

Your present sexual script might have you assuming notions such as these:

- You should play the passive role.
- You should not express any sexual pleasure.
- You expect your man to know how to give you pleasure.
- You always follow your partner's directions.
- You anticipate intercourse each time you're having sex.
- You believe the height of sexual pleasure is nothing short of simultaneous orgasm during intercourse.

These beliefs and others you might be harboring influence how you deal with your sexuality. Coupled with your hormone imbalance, these beliefs may diminish your orgasm experience. I encourage you to be open to challenging your perceptions and beliefs regarding your style of creating an orgasm.

Specifically, how can a hormonal imbalance and other influences impact your orgasm, and what can you do about it? The effects of clitoral stimulation may often be altered by hormonal changes as well as by various side effects of medication. Take this opportunity to explore your "new clitoris" as if for the first time. Self-pleasuring is not only gratifying but an aid to developing your sexuality. "Masturbation is really sexual exercise: It aids the development of sex drive and sexual response. Just as important it helps to develop the mind sexually."[4] (A list of books, Internet links, and products to help enhance your masturbation experience can be found on the book's website.)

Your present traditional orgasm may not consistently reach the peaks of your pre-menopausal ones. Weak or inflexible pelvic floor muscles do not always create a strong enough orgasm to relieve the pressure of built up blood. Your body might signal a need for multiple orgasms to alleviate this blood pooling.

Occasionally women experience extended orgasms*, an interesting compensation for the paradox of weaker orgasms. The muscles involved in maintaining a healthy vagina are also involved in the blood flow that are responsible for these changes. Pelvic floor self-assessment guidelines and strengthening exercises can be found on the book's website. Some women find it difficult to differentiate between the plateau stage (just prior to orgasm) and an extended orgasm. But the confluence of waning orgasm and lengthened plateau stage can create a wonderfully sustained pleasure. These women often feel their actual orgasm is a letdown, suddenly terminating the flow of heightened sensation.

You can generate a stronger release by controlling your orgasms using the stop and start method. The instructions are actually quite simple and pleasurable; they involve teasing your clitoris. Vary the pressure and location of your finger(s) or vibrator/eroscillator near or on your lubricated clitoris, and then hold back when you feel on the edge, close to orgasm. You can do this by taking a few deep breaths and pulling back on the stimulation, and then waiting until your body relaxes and your breathing normalizes. Then increase or reapply the stimulation.

Continue to tease back and forth several times until you finally feel the need to release. The buildup of blood will eventually create a powerful orgasm.

If your usual mode of creating orgasms has been to tighten the area around your crotch or anus, you have been unknowingly restricting the blood flow. By consciously trying to keep this area loose, you may notice more intense and/or multiple orgasms. Relaxation of these muscles will create more space for the blood to pool, which can benefit the intensity of your orgasm.

If you are in need of a slight nudge to get you over the edge (from plateau stage to orgasm), I recommend using a fantasy or potent memory at this point in your orgasm cycle. This could be somewhat akin to a mental imagery orgasm, which uses an orgasmic pathway, one that bypasses the spine. By blending your direct physical stimulation with mental imagery, you could create a unique orgasmic experience. Studies have shown that,

> Orgasm is more than simply a reflex. While it incorporates reflexive components, it also includes perception, which is not a necessary component of true reflexes. Orgasm may be triggered by a number of physical and mental stimuli. It does not even require direct genital stimulation. Mental (imagery-induced) orgasm in women has been demonstrated under laboratory conditions.[5]

The flip side of incredible orgasms are the ones that bring you pain. Pain can come in the form of severe discomfort in the pelvic region and headaches. Pelvic pain can be related to the rigidity or weakness of your pelvic floor. A pelvic floor physical therapy specialist can diagnose and treat your symptoms by designing a personalized exercise program to revitalize your pelvic floor. More information regarding genital pain can be found in Chapter 5. (Listings of practitioners can be found on the book's website.) Headaches can be experienced before, during and after an orgasm. These can be related to muscles contracting in the head and neck area or a spike in blood pressure that causes blood vessels to dilate. If you experience headaches often, it is best to consult with your doctor to make certain it is not related to something more serious.

This chapter has focused on discovering your *Personal Path to Pleasure*. I have provided various exercises to show you how to explore your body and to create sexual pleasure with the challenges of a menopausal body.

Chapter 4 provides information on how to create and maintain an erotically charged connection with your partner. Specific instructions will show you various activities to trigger the desire for sex with your mate.

Chapter 3: Important Points

- It is essential to uncover beliefs regarding sex and specifically masturbation in order to revive or create your *Personal Path to Pleasure.*
- It is crucial to understand the origin of your inner voice in order to break free of it.
- Developing your *Personal Path to Pleasure* begins with knowing your body.
- Viewing your body as a holistic entity is an integral aspect of reclaiming your sexual pleasure.
- Learning about your genitalia is a crucial step to creating sexual pleasure.
- Knowing the beliefs you hold regarding masturbation is important for understanding what is hindering your self-pleasure enjoyment.
- Self-pleasuring is not only gratifying but an aid to developing your sexuality.
- Exploring your sensual body not only with your hands, but with other parts of your body and sexual aids.
- An extremely important aspect of the *Personal Path to Pleasure* is discovering your present erogenous zones and learning how to create new ones.
- Your entire body has the capacity to feel heightened sensations.
- How you create orgasms will continuously fluctuate as you age.
- Personal sexual scripts influence your fantasies and how you create and perceive pleasure.

4

HOW TO TURN ON WITH A PARTNER: CREATING AND SUSTAINING AN EROTICALLY CHARGED CONNECTION

I would like to stress that even a healthy libido is not enough to produce the wanting of intimate sex. This chapter introduces erotic connections*, which contribute an essential ingredient to creating passionate sex. These connections comprise an extended trigger phase. As your sex drive (lustful appetite) wanes, they take an even more important role in creating the wanting of sex and become the thread that binds all the phases of the *Sexual Pleasure Model* together. The following guide will show numerous ways to fire your sexual spark and sustain this erotic charge between you and your mate throughout the day.

Follow the 3 E's—Explore, Experiment and Enjoy!

My major role as sexologist is that of "permission giver." I hold no judgment, granting you the opportunity to explore your sexual expressions and behaviors—without guilt and without shame, as long as what you are doing is legal. Note that some areas have laws relating to marijuana, sex toys, explicit sex videos or books, acts of oral and/or anal sex. A listing of U.S. state and worldwide laws pertaining to these acts and materials can be found on the book's website.

The suggestions below are my version of the all-familiar mantras we read about in inspirational texts or hear bellowed from the pulpits of motivational speakers. They are all interpretations of sacred writings, with my own sexual spin added. They represent a powerful blueprint for life and especially for developing your *Personal Path to Pleasure*. Please make them your own by expressing them in a language that resonates with you and can easily be set to memory.

- Listen to Cues: Listen to your heart, your brain, your breath, and your genitals. They might be "screaming" or barely audible, but they are never silent. They are always there to guide you. Listen to your lover's cues; they will inform your next kiss or expression of affection.
- Be Present: Focus on the moment, what is happening now, not yesterday, not tomorrow, not outside the bedroom door. You will miss life if you are not living it for the now. You might miss the glint in your lover's eyes.
- Release: Liberate yourself from suffering and sadness; forgive others (important—this does not mean you condone their actions), forgive yourself (learn from your errors and move on). Release everything that is keeping you from moving forward. Release everything that is keeping happiness at bay. Release everything that is keeping erotic pleasure out of the bedroom.

These sayings are simple but demand a fair amount of attention to achieve. They are important words to remember, especially when you are interacting with your loved one. As a dear friend once said to me, "I might not be able to be with you 100% of the time, but when I am, I'll give you 150% of me."

Discuss these sayings with your partner, and share your thoughts on the cues you both do well and ones that could use improvement. What will help keep you focused? What distracts you? Have you carried a burden that would be diminished if you forgave him? Would self-forgiveness lessen your suffering? In expressing these thoughts and sharing them with your spouse, you will most likely hear some of his concerns. This type of discussion creates an intimacy that is often considered an aphrodisiac by some women. Such discussions will also help build and reinforce the foundation of your relationship in a way that even long-term connections can benefit.

Spontaneous Erotic Thoughts and Fabricated Fantasies

Perhaps when you were younger and your hormones were raging, you thought about sex often, or at least more often than you do now. You might have become one of those women who lament that their libido has disappeared. This feeling usually refers to an important element that you were unaware of until it ceased to exist—your sex drive (unconscious trigger). It is comprised of innate emotional and physical components that "silently" trigger an interest in sex. The following domino effect produces the desire to act sexually if your body generates and converts all the signals properly:

- <u>sex drive</u> (spontaneous erotic thoughts or innate physical sensations) leads to ...
- <u>sexual arousal</u>, interest in sex (physical), which leads to ...
- <u>sexual desire</u>, interest in sex (emotional), which leads to ...
- interest in acting sexually

Or:

- <u>sex drive</u> (spontaneous erotic thoughts or innate physical sensations) leads to ...
- <u>sexual desire</u>, interest in sex (emotional), which leads to ...
- <u>sexual arousal</u>, which leads to ...
- interest in acting sexually

However, your once dependable unconscious erotic thoughts may have virtually disappeared as your hormones changed,[1] leaving you with no trigger and producing a sense of low libido.

"I want my mojo back" was exactly how Angela described her reason for consulting with me. Her story went something like this:

I have been flying cross-country on business for years. The best part is when I'm seated next to a handsome man. Mind you, I'm married so I never flirt. But his mere presence has me daydreaming about unimaginable sexual acts that always turn me on. Of course he has no idea these fantasies are running through my head, and I never let on. If I am on my way to a business meeting, the flight always seems too short. But if my husband Sidney is waiting for me, it feels like I have prepared for sex even before seeing him. Recently I noticed all that has changed. At first, I thought, maybe I'm no longer being seated next to handsome men or maybe I'm too tired to fantasize—I seem to fall asleep quickly on flights these days. I keep making excuses, but I know my body does feel different lately. I'm missing my sexy thoughts. Honestly, I don't know what is happening, but it certainly isn't happening down there— [as she points to her genitals].

Perhaps you can relate to her earlier memories. You might have even taken it further back then and become a member of the "mile-high club," having sexual intercourse in flight.

When your heartthrob or typical triggers are no longer prompting unconscious sexual thoughts or spontaneous physical sensations, it is time to get more proactive. By incorporating external aphrodisiacs into your repertoire, you are likely to produce the physical sensations to feel turned on. If you have never used erotica before, or wish to find new material to add to your repertoire, consult the annotated listings on the book's website. A few suggestions:

- While snuggling with your hubby, hot buttered popcorn close by and you in charge of the remote, view explicit sex videos, romantic movies, sexy animated films, any style of moving picture that turns you on.
- Glance through books or websites filled with erotic photographs and paintings and search for images that turn you on. You can find a variety of pictures from vintage to contemporary, and ones depicting all types of fetishes. Even the old masters painted nudes and mythological creatures in the act of love.

- There are numerous websites devoted to erotic comics and sexy sex-ed cartoon visuals. Websites are listed in the book's website.
- Read silently or aloud the erotic "classics" and newer erotic anthologies, short stories, or a novel that has extremely spicy sections.
- Visit the romance or erotica section of your local bookstores, read the cover blurbs, and select something with steamy content that looks appealing.

Exploring for turn-on material could be a great activity to share with your partner, since he is going to be the recipient of your sexual desire. If you have used these materials in the past but they are no longer working for you, I suggest enjoying the process of discovering new ones.

Give yourself permission to find sexually explicit materials you think might interest you, even exploring ones you have been curious about but too embarrassed to admit to anyone. You might want to try watching lesbian or threesome movies (two women and a man or vice versa). Watching a threesome video and envisioning yourself being pleasured by the other people involved could be rather exciting and trigger an arousal response. Keep in mind that even if you get turned on watching women arouse each other, this does not mean you are a lesbian, bisexual, or anything other than who you feel you are.

Then again, there are some women who have been considered "late-blooming" lesbian-bisexuals. According to psychologist Carla Golden's interviews of these women, they:

> ...described their heterosexual pasts in terms of repression and falsehood. Another subset maintained that though they had, in fact, been "truly" heterosexual in the past, they were just as "truly" bisexual or lesbian now.... They typically described the onset of their same-sex desires as strong, spontaneous, and surprising.[2]

If you feel any confusion after being exposed to these videos, or have been attracted to women and it is creating conflict in your life, I strongly suggest you meet with a therapist that specializes in relationships. The book's website has listings of therapists and organizations that can link you to an appropriate person.

There is also no harm in viewing various extreme sexual activities that have the potential to turn you on, even if you are quite certain you do not wish to try them. If you are interested in using erotica to turn yourself on but you're being hindered by feelings of shame, consider the possibility of changing your thoughts and responses to this material. By finding the root cause of your shame and subsequently changing your attitude towards erotica, you will be able to welcome the physical turn-on you experience and convert it to an interest in sex and/or sexual desire. (Chapter 3, Sleuthing Out Your Shame, Exercise 1 will help you change your attitude regarding erotica.) It may also help to investigate different types of erotica—some types may not trigger a "shame" response but still have the desired effect of enhancing your interest in sex.

The following is an extreme example, but it illustrates how even an unlikely situation has the ability to arouse. At the Erotic Literary Salon, I was exposed for the first time to the subgenre of homoerotica (male-male) created by and for women readers. All the women at the Salon who wrote and read this type of work considered themselves part of a heterosexual couple. And even though this subject turned them on, these women identified as straight.

As you age, you might find the soft-core, innuendo-filled erotica no longer a turn-on. There is no shame in delighting in hard-core explicit material or the generating of intense fantasies that can ensue— so, enjoy!

According to the 2004 International Sexual Fantasy Research Project comprised of 3,433 completed American surveys and a total of 20,153 British and American adults, more than 90% of adults fantasize regularly and 60% of women use pornography. Research participants gave the following reasons for creating fantasies:[3]

1. Fantasies help me to relieve boredom.
2. Fantasies cheer me up when I am depressed.
3. Fantasies allow me to perform acts that I cannot do in real life.
4. Fantasies permit me to have sex with people whom I would not or could not have sex with in real life.
5. Fantasies permit me to explore different sexual thoughts and activities.
6. My partner becomes more attractive to me in my fantasies.
7. Fantasies help me to become aroused with my partner or partners.
8. I cannot help myself. The fantasies just pop into my mind.
9. Fantasies are preferable to actual sexual experiences.
10. Fantasies make the outside world go away.

You might relate to the following three reasons why some women construct sexual fantasies. I have included examples from my clientele and how they have used fantasies to cope with some of their issues. These labels came from a list of fourteen reasons that Brett Kahr identified in his International Sexual Fantasy Research Project.

1. Wish-Fulfillment (conscious or unconscious): To get aroused and/or create a climax. Barbara, an imaginative client, confided that thinking about a specific teacher always turned her on. When she was having difficulty climaxing, she would envision her teacher's hands pleasuring her.
2. Trial Action: To change sexual thoughts that cause us conflict in real life. Karen, a shy client, felt squeamish when performing fellatio, so she envisioned her husband's penis as an ice cream cone. The enjoyment of her ice cream fantasy transferred over into pleasure when sucking his penis.
3. Avoidance of Painful Reality: To help stay focused on sex. Anita had suffered from personal loss and found it difficult to create and sustain a sexual longing when her thoughts constantly drifted elsewhere. Using an intense sexual fantasy helped her to focus on pleasure by helping her replace negative thoughts that kept intruding in her personal sexual space.

An enormous selection of erotically charged material is available on the Internet and in stores. The content ranges from innuendo styles to explicitly charged erotica. The focus also spans male-centric to women-centered porn, ethical porn* and amateur porn*. There is an overlap of terminology when it comes to various genres of explicit sex. But this information is only relevant if you are trying to locate a certain style. What is essential if you decide you want to get turned on by porn is that you find material that stimulates you. You could share it during sexplay or access it prior to your partner's arrival, sparking your desire for sex in advance of your sexual connection.

There is a relatively new style of erotically charged material that blends meditation, visualization, and suggestion techniques to create a Directed Erotic Visualisation© (DEV©).[4] It has the potential to ultimately arouse and produce orgasms. (Self-disclosure: While experiencing a custom designed DEV© that incorporated my own erotic triggers and sexual behavior preferences, I elicited a most powerful "thought" orgasm.[5] Detailed information on this technique and how to access free audio stories as well as purchase personalized and general DEV©s can be found on the book's website.

As mentioned previously, it is necessary for you to feel comfortable with the thought of thinking about viewing, listening to, and/or reading sexually explicit content in order to become emotionally turned on. Otherwise even if you are showing signs of physical arousal, your unconscious will most likely not convert this to emotional sexual desire.

Another method of using erotica involves an indirect turn-on. This will only work if your partner enjoys graphically charged material.

Have him choose a genre that will widen his eyes and awaken his erotic spirit. Be aware that depending on his physical condition, you might need to stimulate him manually while he gazes at the screen or page. The combination of arousing simultaneously the visual and physical senses will most likely trigger his sexual turn-on, even if he doesn't get a hard penis. You can also tell him erotic stories or fantasies of your own creation.

For this method, your role will be to focus on your partner as he gets turned on. The material will act as an intermediary to the arousal feedback loop* that it initiates, which most likely will trigger your own path to pleasure. There are numerous options for making this style of enhancement work. While your partner is watching, listening to, and/or reading sexually explicit material, face him and note his responses. The two of you might consider fondling each other simultaneously or separately, even if he doesn't need it to feel aroused. I suggest you set up this scenario wherever you both feel comfortable expressing sexual responses. Ask your partner to indicate his pleasure through sounds, differentiated breathing, and/or facial expressions, allowing you to become aware of his feelings and to get sexually excited by his erotic sparking. Once you are turned on, you can encourage your partner to divert his gaze from the sexual material to you. Verbally ask for his attention or physically create the scene for this exchange of focus, and then you will become the object of his desire.

Using your sexually excited partner as an aphrodisiac for yourself sets up an arousal feedback loop whereby you get each other turned on. Most often this is created unconsciously during sexplay, but in this instance you are deliberately using an external stimulus to jumpstart the cycle. This is a loop that continues to feed your sexplay once ignited. I encourage you to explore different scenarios using sexually explicit material as a secondary external aphrodisiac, especially if you are not interested in using this material personally.

Another path to creating an interest in sex is exchanging sexual fantasies or sex stories; the process can be both enlightening and entertaining. You could conjure up older fantasies/stories from your memory or decide as a couple to exchange ones from similar time periods, such as teen years, 20s, or present time. Take turns using some of the following phrases to activate your erotic thoughts:

- I'm curious how it would feel …
- I've always wondered …
- I would really like to know how…
- I would never really want to do this, but I've been thinking about…

Prior to exchanging fantasy stories, follow these guidelines.

- Make certain neither of you passes judgment verbally or exhibits critical facial expressions while your partner is sharing their story.
- Make it clear if you actually would like to recreate the fantasy scene you are sharing—soon, in the future, or not at all.
- Don't offer any verbal feedback while your partner is speaking, unless asked to do so or if you wish something clarified.
- At the end of your spouse's story you can continue it with your fantasy or create your own.

While on vacation, my clients Marsha and Fred decided initially to share sex stories based on a threesome. They tossed a coin to determine who would go first and Marsha won. She mentioned that this was a story she didn't wish to duplicate.

> As I slipped my slinky red, "take me now" dress over my hips, I felt your lips graze my nape from behind. "Oh, my!" I whispered and melted a bit as I drew my arm back and cupped your hardness. You let out a groan of pleasure that held me back a sec, but I finally let go and proceeded to strut out the door. All the while consciously aware you were eyeing my butt, so I continued to exaggerate the sway in my walk.

> Our elegant hotel bar set the stage for our ménage à trois. I entered alone, continuing my sway as I eyed the overfilled room—happy hour. A sundrenched form sat tall, back to bar. His lips pressed gently against the crystal, eyes shining above the rim, catching mine as I came close enough to feel his heat. He barely moved as I maneuvered my way between him and the woman trying fruitlessly to get his attention. In my practiced sultry voice, I asked, "Would you suggest a drink to cool the air and fire my soul?" His demeanor expressed both a bit of shock and pleasure as he smiled a knowing smile and extended his arm only slightly so I had to come closer. "Terrance," a British accent whispered in my ear as his free arm pulled me closer, and I melted into his voice.

Our bodies shouted "where to next?" But we continued to "dance" a banter with stolen touches until you placed an arm around my shoulders. Terrance cautiously stepped back to survey the scene. He had already made my pants wet as you introduced, "the husband" your voice trying to be angry as you pulled me toward you. He later mentioned that our smiles gave our game away.

Terrance played along and we found ourselves in bed, me surrounded by two fine bodies wanting to please. An unspoken rule became most apparent as you emptied my drawers searching for scarves. After tying my limbs gently to the four-posted bed I was told not to touch only to enjoy the pleasures of both your caresses. Your whisper kisses placed strategically on the dimples and soft lines of my face. Then traveling below to trace a path to my belly button, "oh, how I love the tip of your tongue filling that teeny hole."

You divided your efforts, two hands and teeth exploring my lips below, nibbling, stretching, and sucking, creating sensations I never knew existed. As two hands stroked the webs of my toes and a mouth sucked on each digit. I was in ecstasy on the edge of climax, but neither of you would permit me to come, pulling away as I came close and finally allowing me to explode.

At the end, Marsha was excited to hear Fred elaborate about how he would add different sexual behaviors to the scene.

If you can't conjure up any fantasies/stories but would like to share some to spice up your erotic life, you can always retell an erotic story you read or viewed. Use racy language and inflections to create the desire for sex merely through your style of relaying the story.

You can envision your ideal sexual scene, even ravishment. There is no shame in envisioning this kind of scene; many women fantasize being "taken" by the man of their dreams. It is a rape scene that is controlled by the woman's thoughts. Some women even use fantasy, specifically writing erotica, as a healing tool to overcome sexually painful experiences.[6]

Another option would be to produce a fantasy together, taking turns providing paragraphs, or switching gender roles—you be the male and your partner be the female voice. Develop stories as complex and as hot as you want; remember you are doing this to get turned on. You can even write these fantasies from a distance via email or snail mail, so that when you finally meet your partner the written word will have created an air of anticipation.

Be very clear whether these stories are ones you wish to reenact or just use as turn-ons. A word of caution: do not share any of your fantasies that might be hurtful to your sex partner. For example, you don't want to endow your male character with physical attributes that your partner is lacking.

Keep in mind that most people who enjoy role-play, even bondage / dominance / sadism / masochism (BDSM), are not emotionally damaged goods as the book *Fifty Shades of Grey* implies.[7] The reader response to the book was a revelation; it informed Americans (and I suspect in all countries where it is legal to read) just how many women can be aroused by stories of ravishment and domination. Some of the women readers interviewed stated they enjoyed the words and the turn-ons they received from reading the text, but they would never consider reenacting the scenes. Others admitted the desire to enact similar fantasies. (Chapter 6 has examples of various role-play characters and scenes.)

Acting out sexual scenarios, especially ones of ravishment (being "taken" by someone they actually desire) requires explicit trust on the part of both parties involved. The individual who consents to being ravished is actually in control of the situation, by the mere act of granting permission and setting the scene (parameters) beforehand.

Safe words or gestures should always be used under these circumstances, a form of communication expressing discomfort in the situation and sometimes the need to stop immediately. You can create your own words, or use ones that are commonly recommended such as the colors on a traffic light:

Red – stop
Yellow – proceed with caution
Green – go

If you need to signal someone to stop and you can't speak or would prefer not to have sound as part of the scene, indicate your desire with a gesture or piece of fabric. Keep the cloth in your hand until you need to convey "no," then drop it. Your trusted partner should immediately stop what they are doing, no questions asked. I strongly advise choosing a BDSM primer mentioned in the resource section of this book's website if you are interested in learning more about this style of sexual behavior.

Depending upon your inclination and location (its use is legal in some places), marijuana can help create fantasies and for some women bridge the gap to arousal. There are also special creams and vacuum vibrators (mentioned on book's website) that can engorge your clitoris, which helps induce sexual thoughts and create an internal arousal feedback loop.

Creating Atmosphere for Sexplay

Promise me you won't just read the first sentence. The number one predictor of a good libido at menopause is a new sex partner, even for women who previously felt they had a low libido.[8] This study might suggest that a new partner could revive your desire for sex, but the researchers didn't mention that new relationship energy (NRE) does have a shelf life and sparks eventually wane.

And now you are wondering why I even mentioned this tidbit of information, since you are in a sexually monogamous relationship and a new partner is not an option.

What is important is that the NRE-type of energy can be replicated to generate ORE. Ore is a material that holds within it a valuable mineral; it also stands for Old Relationship Energy. ORE is a solid relationship that has, at its core, energy with the potential to be sparked and surrounded by years of profound shared experiences. You have the latter if you are a couple that have been together for years, but it is the erotic connection that is necessary to create an enduring ORE. The following recommendations will guide you in creating and sustaining an ORE. (NRE and ORE are terms borrowed from the polyamorous* community.)

Sparking your libido starts much earlier than falling into each other's arms in bed. Flirting, gazing, those actions similar to when you first met, are all part of the conscious trigger component of the *Sexual Pleasure Model*. It might seem awkward initially, especially if you have not done this for a while, but after repeated practice it will begin to feel natural again. Let the memories of your initial encounter help create and sustain your erotic connection*.

Set aside a specific timeframe for sexplay—as with a date, you need time to create an interest in sex. Many couples believe sexual desire is a natural process, but it wasn't even when you first dated. Think back on the time you spent anticipating what you were going to do together and your preparation for the big day. The build-up prior to the date is all part of the sparking process. You can view this occasion as a tryst, when lovers come together solely for pleasuring.

Once on your date, you can be comforted knowing this time period will be devoted solely to pleasuring each other. If one of you happens to be angry when you have scheduled this sexplay period, use this time to hold hands and discuss the anger issue. But if anger often hijacks sexplay, discuss why this occurs so frequently, since it can be a sign of a larger underlying problem. (A sexual health professional could be instrumental in helping you deal with this issue.)

Scenarios for Sparking your Libido and Sustaining Your Erotic Connection

Becoming more intimate outside the bedroom will help build intimacy inside it. I suggest learning something you both know little to nothing about, but have a mutual interest in exploring. Brainstorm together, presenting the most extreme and absurd ideas and then working backwards to find one or more you are both interested in pursuing. Nothing should be excluded or mocked. Classes might be considered in sky diving, golf, snorkeling, meditation, photography, painting, cooking, learning to fly, camping, and so on.

I am a social dancer, enjoying various styles of dancing that require a quick lesson or two, but basically simple couples dancing. If dancing in public makes you feel uncomfortable, then just do it with your partner in private, maybe naked by the fireside—my erotic dream.

Actually, this is one I have partially realized—sans fireplace, extremely erotic and definitely was a libido sparker.

I have heard several comments on the dance floor that might get you interested in dancing, especially if this has not been an otherwise appealing activity. After dancing a particularly wonderful waltz, where my dance partner and I were in total sync, in flow, he remarked, "This is better than sex" —and we were not sexual partners or even considering becoming partners.

I personally know of several marriages that have been saved by the couples deciding to take up dancing. It not only involves movement, but touch, leading, and following—"listening" to cues. Dance is often referred to as, "The vertical expression of a horizontal desire." Or as a platonic Zydeco dance friend commented as he held me close, "Remember, this is only a three-minute love affair, and then I move on" (to his next dance partner). I knew he went home to his wife who doesn't dance, probably turned on by the physical intimacy of his dances with me and others.

If you feel totally uncomfortable leading or following in couple form you might consider square dancing, contra or English country dancing (think Jane Eyre). These are cued dances, where the participants move according to the caller's almost continuous verbal directions, often to live music. The latter two dances are flirtatious by nature since they combine gazing and smiling as part of the dance demeanor.

It is not unusual to see committed couples, who are dancing with other partners, flirt with each other while passing. These dances are all about having fun, and you can take it to another level if you are using it as a movement aphrodisiac. Moving in the arms of an unknown dance partner can stir your libido and then you later transfer that feeling to your intended partner. If your partner doesn't like to dance, he can be waiting at home for the libido you charged while dancing.

Phone Sex to Rejuvenate your Libido and Sustain your Erotic Connection

Phone sex is another tool for recreating your earlier days of NRE. Whether you are continents apart or in the next room, creating a stimulating hot phone sex scenario is likely to heighten your erotic energy. A phone conversation may provide you with the safety net needed to explore and share your erotic thoughts since there are no visual cues and distractions. Here are some ideas:

- Discuss details of a sexual encounter you enjoyed together.
- Talk about your ideal sexual encounter with your partner, set the scene with details, and discuss what you would really like to have done to you or do to your partner.
- Read an explicit sex story to your partner.
- Share the contents of an explicit sex movie you watched or perhaps are watching while speaking with your partner.
- You can take this conversation to the point where one of you enters the other person's space (clearly only if you are close by), and then you start fondling each other.
- If you are at a distance and wish to satisfy each other sexually, I suggest head phones to free up hands and spicy conversation. You might even consider Skyping. There are also haptic devices available that can allow you to physically arouse each other by remote control. Listing of products to be found on the book's website.
- Using racy language can take any exchange to another level, creating even more intense erotic sparks. These words may be used during phone sex or during a sexual encounter to keep the arousal loop energized. If you are not comfortable using this language or lack a vocabulary of salacious words, you can find several books that focus on this subject listed on the book's website.

In Bed

The most important aspect of being part of a sexual encounter is to be present. You are thinking that is obvious, but consider how many times your mind wandered into territory having nothing to do with the moment's pleasure. You added to your shopping list while sucking on your partner's penis, recalled a forgotten phone call as your clitoris was being licked, and that all too familiar worry, "Wait, did I remember to turn off the stove?" pops into your mind as he begins to pinch your nipples.

If you find your mind straying or notice your partner's is, I suggest breathing in sync while gazing into each other's eyes. Initially you might have to instigate this verbally with a code word or touch, but at some point it will come naturally, noticing each other's cues via gaze and or breathing. Use this technique to get in touch with each other's erotic energy. (Followers of Neo-Tantra may practice a more ritualized form. The book's website lists written materials, DVDs and workshops on Neo-Tantra.)

I stumbled upon our "word" as I noticed my partner was wandering in thought. I called him on it, and he was most honest. He was thinking about how to varnish a painting. Now all we have to do is mention "varnish" when we think the other is lost in thought, and it brings us back or we start breathing in sync. It is a bit of a joke when we hear the word in public, so we usually have a smile on our faces, but no one is offended. It is sometimes difficult to stay focused, especially during a long session of loving.

Specifically, when you are dealing with issues of sexual desire, it is crucial to be able to concentrate all your energies on creating pleasure. It is pleasure that drives the wanting. It is not unusual for people to be sexually intimate without considering what external distractions might divert their attention elsewhere.

Each person has different requirements for creating a setting that will support being present. Certain noises, smells and lighting—all can be distractors or turn-ons, depending upon your specific preferences. You will learn what these are with experience; they will also need to be ones you both agree upon since you are participating as a couple to create a pleasurable sexual encounter. And remember to check the stove before embarking on pleasures of the flesh.

There are thousands of Internet sites specifically focused on helping you create a romantic ambience in your bedroom, often promising a setting that will inspire passion and stimulate your interest in sex. What they fail to address are *your* specific requirements that will spark and sustain your erotic spirit.

The list below will help you determine what conditions will keep you from being distracted, setting the stage for passion and sexplay. Feeling comfortable is an essential ingredient in responding to your partner's overtures in a positive way. This list can be personalized by adding some of your own requirements. Please mark whether a particular condition is significant or insignificant.

Bedroom	Significant	Insignificant
• doors locked	_____	_____
• doors wide open	_____	_____
• lights on	_____	_____
• clean room	_____	_____
• messy room	_____	_____
• phones sound off	_____	_____
• phone out of room	_____	_____
• scented room	_____	_____
• no scents in room	_____	_____
• heat	_____	_____
• A/C	_____	_____
• windows open	_____	_____
• windows closed	_____	_____
• music	_____	_____
• no music	_____	_____
• type of music	_____	_____
• candle light	_____	_____
• total darkness	_____	_____
• temperature set at …	_____	_____
• distractions	_____	_____

Personal		
• naked	_____	_____
• lingerie	_____	_____
• cologne	_____	_____
• no cologne	_____	_____
• socks off	_____	_____
• shower/bath	_____	_____

Personal	Significant	Insignificant
• clean hands	_____	_____
• filed fingernails	_____	_____
• teeth cleaned	_____	_____
• wash genitalia	_____	_____
• wash armpits	_____	_____

Now here is the challenge—share it with your partner. See if you are in agreement, and if not, start negotiating.

Mary came to me with a dilemma: her husband of many years was starting to be slovenly in the bedroom. He would come to bed and often didn't shower first. I suggested that prior to confronting him with her concerns she should invite him to shower with her. And also to reinforce the pleasure she received from his fresh scent, she could tell him how wonderful he smelled all the while lovingly drying his body. At her next session with me, she described how she handed him the towel once he was dried, in a motion that asked him to do the same for her. It has become a ritual since her last session, since they have begun showering together daily. Sometimes "negotiating" can take many forms and finding a creative solution can bring unexpected results.

Personal Pleasure Sex "Bucket" List

I have provided a sample sex list for creating your personal pleasure sex bucket. You can extend the project and assist your partner in creating one for himself and then combine to develop a couple's pleasure sex bucket list. Make certain you do not coerce or pressure each other while evaluating how you each wish to proceed. Use the following evaluation categories to classify the items on the sex list.

Evaluation Categories

1. Behaviors you definitely wish to try
2. Behaviors you would consider trying if your partner were interested
3. Behaviors you are not interested in but would negotiate if your partner were interested
4. Behaviors you are definitely not interested in even trying

Sex List

- threesome with two men and one woman
- threesome with two women and one man
- oral sex
- vaginal penetration penis
- vaginal penetration dildo
- anal penetration penis
- anal penetration dildo (flanged)
- butt plug inserted
- use of vibrator/Eroscillator
- nipple clamps
- tied up
- cane
- edging*
- flogger
- whip
- paddle
- ropes
- feather tickler
- pegging*
- blindfolded
- hands tied
- feet tied
- light spanking
- heavy spanking
- phone sex
- sex in shower
- masturbate with partner
- silent sex
- loud sex

- group sex
- sex with partner while someone watches
- partner has sex with other person while you watch
- have sex with other person while partner watches
- sexplay in bed all day
- keep lights on bright
- dimmed lights
- darkness
- have your partner list positions they would like to try
- go to a strip club
- take a Neo-Tantra workshop
- go to sex party
- go to swinger's party
- go to BDSM party
- go to dungeon
- wear sexy lingerie
- wear penis ring
- pole dancing/belly dancing
- explicit texting with partner
- take nude photos
- take videos of having sex
- take videos of self while masturbating
- toes sucked
- kissing during sex
- getting couples massage
- sexplay with no intercourse
- sexplay with no orgasm
- biting during sexplay
- sexplay in location where you could be seen or get caught
- rimming* with fingers
- rimming with tongue

- have sex in different places within house

Many of these behaviors came from a study on sexual diversity in the United States.[9] Please feel free to personalize the list by adding more behaviors and scenarios.

Revisit your evaluations on a regular basis or just allow for spontaneous change. My son's nursery school teacher taught me an excellent phrase that I use to this day, even though my son has reached adulthood. I use it with him, my clients, and I even remind myself, "You are allowed to change your mind." Some people make decisions and feel committed to them, even hemmed in by them. They feel obligated to pursue their original goal at all cost, even though their interests have changed. Do consider all decisions flexible when your emotions are involved.

You've made your "sexual choice," and now be willing to respond to the overtures of your partner even if you initially do not feel sexually turned on. This will allow you to change the focus of viewing your partner as the initiator of sex, to one of facilitator to your own sexual arousal and desire.

If you are snuggling in the arms of your partner with no thoughts of sex and he is exhibiting signs of sexual desire, you can choose to be sexual. Ask to be turned on (seduced), even if you don't initially feel any interest in behaving sexually. This is when your discussions regarding behavior preferences and conditions are drawn into action.

When I asked women in my focus groups what behaviors typically aroused them, kissing was at the top of the list. An aside, as we age our gums change, our digestive system becomes more sluggish, all can lead to unpleasant breath.

Consider keeping mouth refreshed; brush teeth, brush tongue, and use a mouthwash then rinse. (Unless your partner enjoys the taste of chemicals.)

If you have not been kissing your partner because his breath has altered, you need to approach him gently. Telling someone they have bad breath in our culture is not easy. You might want to approach the subject by saying in your own words, "I love kissing you, except lately your breath has not been pleasant. I'm concerned since it could be a health issue." If you have both read this book you can have a good laugh about bad breath, but ultimately if you have not been kissing figure out why and pucker up.

Discuss the possible reasons: upset stomachs, post nasal drip, gum disease (could be sign of heart disease), and consider suggesting a visit to the dentist or cardiologist. It can also be just large amounts of garlic. Households that enjoy garlicky meals would be best to have fresh parsley served after a meal; it refreshes the breath naturally.

Joan Price recalls how she and her partner used kissing to get in the mood.

> We kissed quietly without disconnecting, paying attention to each other's breath. It slowed us down, quieted our minds, and made us aware of each other and of our own pleasure centers. Our breathing got in sync, and as we continued to kiss, something magical happened. We felt we were melting into each other, one body, one breath. Our skin started tingling, our pleasure receptors came alive. We felt each other shudder with excitement, and we were making love.[10]

Just reading this passage and fantasizing about my lover's luscious kisses, I began to feel a desire to recreate this experience.

While sharing your newfound erogenous zones, remember to express your pleasure and respond in a manner that will reveal your feelings. Various sounds, gazes, breathing patterns, movements can all indicate the pleasure (sometimes displeasure) of your experience. Your responses will create a human aphrodisiac, initiating the arousal feedback loop with your partner.

Do not think of sexual desire and arousal as something that happens only at the beginning of a sexual session. They are necessary elements that need to be sparked continually throughout sexplay in order to keep the erotic energy alive. Desire and arousal ebb and flow, particularly when your sex drive is sluggish. Your interest in sexplay can also wane, especially when distracting thoughts steal your attention. It is most important to communicate your desires clearly throughout sexplay, informing your partner of your need for varying styles of stimulation.

Sounds of pleasure are usually not that difficult to express, but how do you deal with displeasure when you would like to offer a directive for change? "I" messages that express how you feel without blaming your partner are best. Always start your request with a positive comment. Please paraphrase your own requests along the lines of the following examples:

- I love the feel of your hands on my body, and I would prefer if you used your fingers instead of your toes to caress my breasts
- I really like the pressure you are using, but would prefer you alternate between this light pressure and a stronger one.

Don't assume anything; it often works against you especially in bed. I recall having a man pleasuring me with his tongue. He was quite a clitoral connoisseur and giving me much pleasure. I assumed he must be exhausted since I thought I was taking too long. Trying to make him more comfortable, I expressed my satisfaction and asked to change positions. We spoke afterwards and he voiced his disappointed—he had wanted to pleasure me longer with his tongue. I never assumed again.

Hard penises are usually a sign your man is turned on, except for the "woody," the morning hard penis. This occurs as part of the normal sleep cycle during the REM part when there is a surge of blood to the penis. Coincidentally, between 4:00-6:00 a.m. testosterone levels are at their highest. How a morning hard-on translates to desire for sex has all to do with who is sleeping next to him. Men also make choices about whether they wish to turn their arousal (hard penis) into sexual desire, but from anecdotal evidence, more easily than women do with their own arousal.

The urgency of his caress is often a sure sign he is interested in sexual pleasure. Skin tone and facial expressions (another good reason to leave the lights on, besides a visual turn-on), breath changes (especially holding of breath), muscle tension, hard nipples, hand signals are all cues that are to be observed. Of course, his words are most helpful too. You are also encouraged to direct the dance of your own pleasure with similar cues.

Body Image

During my focus groups, many women were concerned about how their sex partners viewed them physically. They knew the impact aging and gravity has had on their bodies, the addition of wrinkles and sagging skin where once shapely figures stood. They feared these changes would interfere with their partner's desire for them. Some women created obstacles so they would not be seen while having sex, covering themselves with blankets and lights out. There were even women who avoided expressing any interest in sex because they feared rejection. Perhaps this scenario resonates with your concerns about your own body image.

Having a conversation with your partner about your concerns regarding your physical appearance is most important, since these concerns could disrupt your sexual turn on. This conversation might be best had when you are sharing the exploratory exercise in Chapter 3. If your partner's looks have changed also and he is no longer as physically appealing, you have several solutions to consider. If you have both added extra weight, and/or are out of shape, your health has probably also been impacted negatively.

Exercise has been known to positively affect both women's and men's libidos. You could suggest a lifestyle change as a couple, one that isn't difficult to follow, no drastic diets or heavy exercise plans, a change for life. Consult a nutritionist and/or trainer, sometimes covered by health insurance. Or you can search the Internet for realistic food plans and exercises. This could be viewed in a similar vein as the dancing I suggested earlier or learning/doing something new together, a bonding experience.

If you are uncomfortable being naked in front of your partner, even after doing the earlier "Head to Toe: Thoughts and Memories" exercise in Chapter 3, or if you just prefer clothing while enjoying sexplay, purchase some sexy lingerie, the type not meant for sleeping in but for turning your partner on. I recommend different styles of lingerie that signal your preference for specific types of sexual behaviors: one type/color wanting a gentle style of loving and another to initiate more aggressive behaviors. You could also wear your sexy lingerie on days you would be willing to be turned on and more tame styles to denote just a cuddle. There are endless varieties of lingerie to denote all types of sexplay.

While in casual conversation with Sharon and Frank, a couple who had just participated in my Ageless Sex workshop, I was privy to an interesting revelation. Sharon mentioned in a concerned tone of voice that she had been gaining weight since menopause. Sharon was far from overweight and said she had always been on the thin side. Frank reacted with a smile and said, "Thank goodness, now I have something to hold onto." She glared back at him and a heated interchange ensued regarding her reasons for staying thin. Sharon had assumed he liked her that way, since she often caught him glancing at thin women.

Frank reminded Sharon that he always complimented her appearance, but she never accepted it. Instead she would say things like, "You always think I look pretty even if I don't." Sharon now realized it was she that wasn't feeling pretty, even though her husband thought she was quite attractive and the added weight made her feel even better to his touch. We finally parted, and I watched them stroll on to the next workshop holding on to each other with renewed interest. Sharon's acceptance of her weight brought out a self-confidence that made her shine. And Frank responded as if he were in the arms of a new lover.

What I have noticed is that what people like visually might not necessarily be what they enjoy holding onto in bed. I learned this personally when I had my first chubby lover. Visually he was not a real turn-on, but in bed, felt like I was snuggled up to a lovable teddy bear. When I shared my story with other women, they tended to agree but felt there was a double standard. What they failed to do was ask their husbands how they felt, or perhaps like Sharon didn't believe them.

This chapter presented specific instructions on how to use explicit sex material along with sex stories and fantasies to help trigger an interest in sex. I also addressed scenarios for sparking the libido outside the bedroom and how to personalize the environment inside the bedroom for sexplay. I've showed numerous ways to establish and sustain an erotic connection throughout the day. The sharing of sexplay styles and behaviors, plus the impact of body image was also addressed.

Chapter 5 will deal with physical challenges, demonstrating how possible changes in vaginal wall and pelvic floor function can precipitate a domino effect, creating unwanted pain and ultimately no interest in sex. Specific guidelines to rejuvenate vaginal health and pelvic floor exercises will be presented, along with an introduction to pelvic floor therapy. Innovative techniques to modify sexual behavior and vaginal issues will also be discussed.

Chapter 4: Important Points

- Mantras for developing your *Personal Path to Pleasure* include: listen to cues; be present: focus on the moment; release: liberate yourself from suffering and sadness; and forgive others.

- The sex drive is an unconscious process that activates your arousal system and sexual desire and ultimately an interest in sex.

- Lack of erotic thoughts due to hormonal changes could produce a sense of low libido.

- A domino effect (trigger=>arousal=>desire or trigger=>desire=>arousal) produces the interest to act sexually if your body generates and converts all signals properly.

- When the unconscious trigger of your sex drive is not functioning properly, it is necessary to be proactive. Techniques such as fabricating fantasies and sex stories, or viewing and reading of explicit sex material are all capable of triggering sexual arousal and desire.

- A healthy libido is not enough to produce the wanting of intimate sex. An erotic connection* is an essential ingredient in creating passionate sex.

- There are numerous reasons women consciously create fantasies. Three examples: Wish-Fulfillment: Used to create a climax; Trial Action: The opportunity to experiment with sexual thoughts that cause conflict; and Avoidance of Painful Reality: To help stay focused on sex.

- An arousal feedback loop is initiated when erotica turns on the spouse and his response arouses his wife, and they continue to feed each other's arousal by their positive sexual response.

- The sharing of fantasies and sex stories, along with role-playing, has the potential to trigger arousal.

- Acting out sexual scenarios of ravishment demand explicit trust between partners and the use of safe words and gestures.

- Marijuana can help create fantasies and for some women bridge the gap to arousal.

- The number one predictor of a good libido at menopause is a new sex partner, or to replicate the feeling of NRE—new relationship energy, which can generate ORE—old relationship energy.

- ORE is a solid relationship that has at its core energy with the potential to be sparked and surrounded by years of profound shared experiences. It is the erotic connection that is necessary to create an enduring ORE.

- Sparking a libido starts much earlier than falling into each other's arms in bed. Flirting and gazing are part of the conscious trigger component of the *Personal Path to Pleasure.*
- A specific timeframe for a sexplay date is necessary, since sexual desire is not an automatic process.
- Becoming more intimate outside the bedroom will help build intimacy inside it.
- Phone sex can be utilized to explore and share erotic thoughts and rejuvenate a libido.
- The most important aspect of being part of a sexual encounter is to be present.
- It is important to determine what conditions are distracting and hinder the ability to be present.
- Set the stage for passion and sexplay.
- Feeling comfortable is an essential ingredient in responding to a partner's overtures in a positive way.
- Change the focus of viewing the initiator of sex, to one of facilitator of sexual desire and arousal. This is done by making a "sexual choice" to respond to sexual overtures.
- Create a human aphrodisiac by initiating the arousal loop through the sharing of sexual pleasure.
- Do not think of sexual desire and arousal as something that happens only at the beginning of a sexual session.
- "I" messages that express how you feel without blaming your partner are best to express displeasure with sexual behaviors.
- It is important to have a conversation regarding body imagery, since it can impact the sexual turn on process negatively.
- Exercise has been known to positively affect both women's and men's libidos.
- What people like visually might not necessarily be what they enjoy holding onto in bed.

5

DEALING WITH PHYSICAL CHALLENGES

The World Health Organization's (WHO) working definition of sexual health is: "…a state of physical, emotional, mental and social well-being in relation to sexuality; it is not merely the absence of disease, dysfunction or infirmity. Sexual health requires a positive and respectful approach to sexuality and sexual relationships, as well as the possibility of having pleasurable and safe sexual experiences, free of coercion, discrimination and violence. For sexual health to be attained and maintained, the sexual rights of all persons must be respected, protected and fulfilled."[1]

The Importance of Genital Health:

How the Health of Your Genitals Affects Your Interest in Sex

Genitals are a source of intense sensations, ranging from the highs of ecstasy to the depths of agony. In the midst of lovers' rapture, their stimulated genitalia can even induce an altered state of consciousness. But menopause can create havoc with your sex organs, ultimately compromising your motivation for sex and, for some women specifically, vaginal intercourse. Hormonal balance plays an important role in keeping your genitalia functioning properly, and estrogen depletion following menopause interferes with this process.

Hormone imbalance is a silent epidemic with extremely "loud" symptoms that affect the lives of more than 50% of all menopausal women. However, far fewer are seeking treatment because of their lack of knowledge regarding the consequences of estrogen depletion.[2]

Hormonal alteration can result in a number of physical, psychological, and sexual changes in menopausal women. This chapter focuses on the genitourinary syndrome of menopause,[3] or GSM: the cluster of vaginal, vulvar, and urinary symptoms, the pain they can produce, and various treatments to alleviate it. You will also learn about several other conditions that can produce unpleasant symptoms that make it difficult to generate sexual pleasure.

Part of a menopausal focus group, Linda was discussing her frustration in finding a sympathetic doctor to deal with her pain.

> I remember clearly the first time I had pain—down there, since it was also the first time my husband used Viagra and I used new lube. I applied extra lube, since the Viagra made him super hard and larger than he had been recently. It still felt like sandpaper, so I added a lot more lube.

> The next morning my vagina really itched and felt like it was on fire. I went online for suggestions, and one site recommended inserting garlic, but it burned even more. Then I tried an apple cider vinegar douche, which helped a bit. Finally I headed to the pharmacy where I purchased an OTC yeast infection cream. It seemed to work until I used up the entire tube as directed on the package.

> Thankfully my gynecologist squeezed me in, and I mentioned all the remedies I had tried. She was really condescending, laughing at the natural remedies I found on the Internet plus she definitely didn't approve of the OTC cream. She said there were many types of yeast infections and gave me a prescription for a different cream.

Linda's saga lasted almost a half an hour as she described visiting more than half a dozen gynecologists and specialists over a period of several years since her first encounter with pain. She was prescribed various medications and treatments based on specific symptoms, but they had merely a bandage effect—offering some relief, perhaps but without addressing the problem behind the symptom. An underlying cause had not been established. So various symptoms kept on appearing and in some cases exacerbating the original symptom, which turned out to have more than one cause. Some doctors reacted to her symptoms in rather dismissive terms, since they were often unable to actually see a physical manifestation of her complaints such as nerve damage or sensitivity.

She finally found a gynecologist specializing in pain, who realized she was suffering from GSM along with vulvodynia and lichen sclerosus. When she initially consulted with gynecologists, she was in perimenopause, a phase that is sometimes difficult to identify since it can occur approximately 10 years prior to actual natural menopause (which would happen at an unknown date in the future). Most of the doctors she visited assumed she had everything but GSM, since they were basing her symptoms on age.

When after treatment she was finally informed that her vagina looked healthy, she and husband Ben planned a special evening together. She used extra lube formulated for sensitive vaginas and longer foreplay, as her physician suggested. But when her husband went to enter her, he was blocked: "It felt like he was hitting something hard in me. Like my vagina had set up a barricade," because it had. Her tightened muscles were trying to protect her vagina, with an old memory of pain from GSM that led to vaginismus. She scheduled another visit to her gynecologist, who recommended she consult with a pelvic floor physical therapist for specialized exercises to deal with her vaginismus, and for biofeedback techniques to reprogram her brain.

You might be wondering why it took so many doctor visits to have Linda's pain diagnosed and remedied. The study, "What We Don't Talk About When We Don't Talk About Sex," shows that doctors tend to shy away from asking the questions that make women comfortable in discussing their sexual health issues.[4] This means you have to find a doctor who is not only knowledgeable about your problem, but one who is non-judgmental and at ease with discussing the subject. You need to be proactive and make an appointment specifically to discuss your problem, and not settle for being told that waiting until your annual physical is fine. What your doctor didn't examine might be hidden from sight.

Your partner might also be suffering indirectly, especially if he is witnessing the grimace on your face as he tries to enter your vagina. It is not uncommon for men to tell me, "I don't want to hurt her—what can I do?" (Chapter 6 has guidelines to expand your sexual repertoire.) I would suggest you take him with you on your gynecological visits so he knows firsthand what your issues are, and then he also has the opportunity to ask questions. Or you can ask him what concerns he would like your gynecologist to address, and you will relay his message and the physician's response. He can also make an appointment to visit privately with your physician to discuss his concerns. But don't leave him out. Give him the opportunity to understand and support you in your efforts to regain your sexual health.

Sexual Behaviors and Vulva-Vaginal Pain

In a study of vulvodynia (vulva pain with no identifiable cause),[5] it was shown that women's and men's disclosures to each other, and their partner's perceived empathic response, resulted in greater sexual satisfaction and less stress for both. I believe these findings and outcome could apply to other sex-related pains, even if they don't share similar origins. The common phrase men tend to voice when their partner is in pain during sexplay is something like: "If you want to stop, that's okay," places a burden on the woman to orchestrate changing the interaction. A more empathetic partner would say, "If you're in pain, I want to stop," showing that he is sharing responsibility by expressing his own desire to stop and not inflict more unintentional pain.

The genitourinary syndrome of menopause (GSM), formerly known as vulvovaginal atrophy and atrophic vaginitis, describes a collection of menopausal symptoms and signs associated with physical changes of the vulva, vagina, and lower urinary tract. GSM includes not only genital symptoms (dryness, burning, and irritation) and sexual symptoms (lack of lubrication, shortening and tightening of vaginal canal, discomfort or pain, and impaired function), but also urinary symptoms. These may include urgency, painful or difficult urination, and recurrent urinary tract infections (UTI). Estrogen deficiency often produces GSM symptoms such as reduced elasticity of vagina, increased vaginal pH, vaginal flora changes, vaginal dryness, change in viscosity, vaginal wall thinning, and inflammation of vagina.

GSM has become a medical challenge because it is under-reported by women as well as under-recognized by health-care providers—and, therefore, under-treated. More or less 50% of postmenopausal women experience vaginal discomfort attributable to some form of GSM. Very recent surveys suggest a high enough incidence that healthcare providers should be proactive in helping their patients to disclose the symptoms related to GSM, as well as help them seek adequate treatment when vaginal discomfort is clinically relevant. Women are usually unaware that GSM is a chronic condition with significant impact on sexual health and quality of life. Indeed, sexual difficulties and genitourinary conditions are more prevalent in women with GSM. Yet effective and safe treatment may be available.

Some women experience the following sensations and symptoms during sexplay. These symptoms are most evident during vaginal penetration, but they can also occur without anything entering the vagina that might lead to chafing.

- Dryness
- Itching
- Burning
- Feels like sandpaper
- Tearing
- Stabbing
- On fire
- Soreness
- Stinging
- Rawness
- Throbbing
- Discharge
- Irritation
- Bleeding

GSM is likely the underlying issue when one of these feelings is persistent, with and without vaginal intercourse. The pH factor in the vagina will be consistently above pH of 4.5[6] (even without a vaginal infection), and the vaginal walls are thin and display little elasticity, creating an environment conducive to vaginal fissures and infections. This all adds up to PAIN!!!—extreme discomfort that is exacerbated by penetration and stroking. There is also emotional distress when women are not able to enjoy their once typical style of sexual pleasuring. Yet in a survey of over 4,000 women, 28% of them suffered in silence by not sharing their pain initially with their partners. They were either embarrassed or felt it was a natural part of growing older. Moreover, 58% avoided intimacy and 64% experienced pain (dyspareunia) associated with vaginal penetration.[7]

Some women do not seek treatment due to personal embarrassment, and those that do often end up with physicians who are uncomfortable with sexuality-related issues. Some physicians even ignore or misdiagnose symptoms, leading eventually to costly treatments. Studies of physicians suggest that lack of time or training, fear of embarrassing themselves or their patients, and the physicians' own religious beliefs influence discussion with patients about sexuality-related issues.

> The vagina is a most neglected organ.... Unmet needs include, but are not limited to: long term care of the atrophic changes it will undergo after the menopause [and] ...appreciation and respect of its erotic meaning, as a loving, receptive, «bonding» organ for the couple. The vaginal erotic value is key as a non-visible powerful center of femininity and sexuality, deeply and secretly attractive in terms of taste, scent (together with the vulva), touch and proprioception. The most welcoming: when lubrication, softness and vaginal orgasm award the woman and the partner with the best of pleasures. Prevention of sexual/vaginal abuse is a very neglected unmet need, as well. Who cares?[8]

I do! As a woman who suffered for many years from what I referred to as my hidden disability, it is my mission to provide you with resources and guidance to help you develop a healthy ageless sex life.

Dr. Alessandra Graziottin's "...lightly provocative" paper (excerpt above) carries her powerful message: "Hormonophobia, in women and in physicians, still prevents the majority of women to use postmenopausal lifelong vaginal estrogens." Studies have shown the use of systemic estrogens are beneficial if used as directed.[9] But this needs to be discussed with your physician, since hormones have side effects that might outweigh their benefits for you. They might also not be appropriate, especially if you have a cancer that is estrogen dependent. There are also alternatives to hormone therapy that are mentioned later in this chapter.

You might be one of the more than 50% of menopausal women who suffer from GSM—often with severe pain brought on by your hidden genital areas: your vagina and/or bladder. It has probably destroyed any motivation you once had to replicate an act of beauty and intimacy that at one time brought you much pleasure.

The Domino Effect of Hormone Imbalance and Pain

Hormone imbalance can produce a chain reaction that impacts the complex causes of chronic and recurrent genital pain. The changes of the pelvic floor muscle brought on by estrogen depletion can be painful and can affect the health of the vaginal wall. Genital pain and the influence it has on a woman's relationship and sexual expression can play a major role in her emotional health. Addressing both the physiological and psychological aspects of pain is integral to treatment.[10]

You could even be protecting your vagina by closing off the opening during an involuntary contraction of the pelvic floor muscles, known as vaginismus. This happens when the pubococcygeus (PC muscle) creates an involuntary muscle spasm that can be quite painful. A pelvic floor physical therapist (yes, this is a specialty) can address this issue along with other pelvic floor related problems. These therapists can assist in treatment, using various techniques depending upon the diagnoses. Biofeedback is also used to help you locate the muscles involved in your pain and help you control the "involuntary" spasms. Once the muscles have been identified, the therapist will diagnose and recommend either relaxation through massage for extremely tight muscles or Kegels to strengthen weak ones or perhaps both.

Either type of pelvic floor dysfunction can be associated with incontinence, frequent or urgent or incomplete urination, constipation or straining or pain during bowel movements, and pain or pressure in the vagina or rectum. It is to be noted that your pelvic floor muscle instability and/or spasms can be contributing to lower back pain. Weak, tight, or spastic pelvic floor muscles may be attributed to disuse, trauma, and surgery.

Pelvic floor disorders can also affect the position of the pelvic organs (bladder, uterus, vagina, rectum, small intestine.). The pelvic floor muscles are described in terms of a "hammock" holding these organs in place. When these muscles are weak, they can create a hernia-like disorder known as pelvic floor prolapse (POP), where one or more organs protrudes through the pelvic floor and may stop functioning properly. It is a complex condition, which is frequent in menopausal women (half of all women older than 50 years) because of its relationship to aging and the adverse effect estrogen deficiency has on pelvic floor support.[11] The conditions and symptoms vary depending upon the specific organ prolapse. Here are some associated with this disorder:

- Dragging sensation in the pelvic
- Feeling like your sitting on a ball
- Vaginal spotting or bleeding
- Urinary incontinence or difficulties passing urine
- Recurrent UTIs
- Constipation
- Anal incontinence
- Low back pain
- Discomfort during vaginal penetration

Your physician can diagnose and determine what treatment options are best for you, based on your health and type of prolapse. There are a range of treatments that include lifestyle changes (losing weight, quitting smoking, lifting heavy objects properly or not at all, treating chronic coughs and constipation), topical estrogen, pessary (supportive device similar to a diaphragm) biofeedback, pelvic floor exercises and stimulation, and surgery.

Vulva/vaginal pain that is not related to GSM or other specific disorders is referred to as vulvodynia (unprovoked pain) and is not necessarily associated with hormonal imbalance, since younger women also experience this problem. But the pain is often described in a similar fashion to GSM, making for a confusing diagnosis. It is to be noted that even though vulvodynia refers to vulva/vaginal pain, it is not confined to this area. Some women experience pain on the inside of their thighs, upper legs, around the anus and urethra. Here are typical descriptions of pain caused by vulvodynia:

- Searing sensation
- Soreness
- Throbbing
- Stinging
- Painful intercourse (dyspareunia)
- Aching

Some women experience vulvodynia for the first time after menopause. Others who have had this issue for years sometimes find that hormone imbalance exacerbated their problem. (Childbirth and breast feeding can contribute to vulvodynia.) It has been suggested to treat chronic vulvar pain in menopausal women first with hormone therapy, and if it does not respond follow with vulvodynia treatments. This will ultimately help distinguish between GSM (remedied with topical estrogen) and vulvodynia (controlled by avoiding potential irritants, various at home and medical treatments, and medications based on specific symptoms). Unfortunately, sometimes women suffer from both. Vulvodynia is a mystery and doctors don't know the cause of most forms of this condition; making it a difficult one to treat.

Vestibulodynia (provoked pain), formerly known as vestibulitis since it is located at the vestibule, is pain that usually occurs towards the bottom area of the vulva at the opening to the vagina. The following are possible contributing factors:

- Nerve injury or irritation to the vulva/vestibule
- Chronic yeast infections
- Muscle spasms or weakness of the pelvic floor
- Frequent use of antibiotics
- Allergies or irritation to chemicals
- Genetic disorders
- Sensitivity to certain foods

Dermatosis (skin disease without inflammation) is a skin problem that can get overlooked because some of the symptoms and pain are characteristic of GSM and vulvodynia. One skin disease that is commonly overlooked is lichen sclerosus, an autoimmune disorder that presents as white patches, scars, and adhesions of the vulva. The labia are easily bruised and torn, causing itching, burning, and pain during vaginal penetration. Steroid creams are commonly used to treat this condition.

However, hormone alterations may cause variety of skin diseases, and some even aggravated by estrogen therapy.[12] "It's complicated." In my opinion, "complicated" is often an overused term but in this instance is most appropriate. If your physician has ruled out the obvious issues based on your symptoms, and you are still in pain, consider consulting a dermatologist/gynecologist who can diagnose for skin diseases.

For some women, the pain never stops and seems to have escalated and infused other areas surrounding the original pain. Chronic pelvic pain (CPP) syndrome is a pain that lasts more than six months and often overshadows the problem that originally caused the pain. This occurs when new "pain generators" develop in the surrounding area, and this painful section becomes overly sensitive. CPP pain may have started with one of the problems listed above but now has evolved to include muscles, the nervous system, surrounding soft tissues, and occasionally other organs in the pelvis. Sometimes the original pain has gone away and the chronic pain becomes the disease.[13]

The nature of this syndrome can involve several different problems that have now been incorporated to contribute to CPP. Therefore, a treatment plan must address all issues involved, using an integrative approach to target the multidimensional aspect of these complex conditions.

Behavioral Modifications/Prevention Tips/Treatments

The following treatments and prevention suggestions can address some of the symptoms related to GSM and vulvodynia. Consult with your health care provider to make certain you are not suffering from any internal infections, since some of these suggestions might mask a more serious underlying condition making it difficult to diagnose properly.

Prior to consulting with your provider, take note of what things make your pain better or worse. If you feel that certain foods, clothing, or environmental factors might be involved, keep a daily diary. Make certain you provide a thorough history and make sure that your doctor performs an internal examination prior to prescribing medications. Complications can arise in diagnosing vaginal health problems, since GSM can lead to symptoms similar to vaginal infections caused by yeast or bacteria. Then again, GSM creates an environment that allows these infections to spread easily, another "it's complicated" situation. The following suggestions are for home procedures that you might want to try before consulting with your doctor.

- Try cold compresses. Cool compresses placed directly on your external genital area may help lessen pain and itching.
- Soak in a sitz bath. Two to three times a day, sit in comfortable, lukewarm (not hot), or cool water for 5 to 10 minutes.
- Avoid tight fitting pantyhose and nylon underwear. Tight undergarments restrict airflow to your genital area, often leading to increased temperature and moisture that can cause irritation. Wear white, cotton underwear to increase ventilation and dryness, and sleep without underwear at night. Wash underwear in detergent free from dyes and perfumes.
- Avoid using perfumed lotions or douches or other products on the labia and in the vagina.
- Avoid hot tubs and soaking in hot baths. Spending time in hot water may lead to discomfort and itching.

- Avoid activities that put pressure on your vulva, such as biking or horseback riding.
- Use white, unscented toilet paper.
- Wash gently. Washing or scrubbing the affected area harshly or too often can increase irritation. Use plain water to gently clean your vulva with your hand and pat the area dry.
- Do not use vaginal wipes.
- Pat the area dry after rinsing or urinating.
- Use vaginal lubrication prior to penetration.
- Apply vaginal moisturizer daily to the external genital areas.
- Try these supplements: Vitamin A, beta carotene, B vitamins, omega-3 fatty acids.
- Try an OTC antihistamine at bedtime. This may help reduce itching and help you rest better. Please keep in mind that this will probably lead to drier vagina. You will need to use more lubricant if you plan to have vaginal penetration.
- Avoid friction or sitting for prolonged periods.
- To relieve burning after penetration, use a glass or stainless-steel wand—cool it in the fridge for vaginal insertion. Or try a vaginal dilator iced in the freezer first, or a plain water homemade popsicle. The book's website has a listing of where to purchase wands and dilators.
- Here's a regimen to help maintain a healthy vulva and vagina: moisturize the skin of the vulva and vagina, massage the vulva, and perform a vibrating massage of the vagina. (Vibrating massage can set off nerve endings for some women.) The restoration of moisture helps eliminate itching, burning and other sensations related to pain during intercourse. A detailed description of this regimen can be found on the book's website.

- Purchase a plastic speculum for personal use: This instrument will allow you to see inside your vagina, access your vaginal walls, and monitor your response to any remedies you have been prescribed or self-prescribed. It will give you the opportunity to observe any changes that may occur due to estrogen depletion and perhaps better understand any unusual sensation that might be attributed to these changes. A link to purchase a speculum can be found on the book's website.

- Use it or lose it: Some physicians believe the "use it or lose it" motto can also work—that is, that regular vaginal intercourse over earlier decades of life can protect a woman from pain when she eventually goes through menopause. But if you are reading this book you have probably passed this stage if you are in pain. You also need to be aware this doesn't work for all women.

The following suggestions are ones you should discuss with your doctor.

- Vitamin E—suppositories
- Topical estrogen,[14] intravaginal tablets, intravaginal rings (The Women's Health Initiative study determined that the use of estrogen creams did not elevate the risk of cardiovascular disease or cancer in women 50-79.)
- Systemic hormonal therapies (oral, transdermal, implant under skin, gel applied to skin)
- MonaLisa Touch laser: A painless and minimally invasive FDA-approved treatment that restores vaginal health. It is used to treat dryness and the loss of vaginal elasticity that can cause mild urinary incontinence, itching, burning, and other painful sensations during intercourse. More information can be found on the book's website.

According to the North American Menopause Society (NAMS), first-line treatment for vaginal atrophy should include non-hormonal vaginal lubricants and moisturizers, as well as continued sexual activity. Vaginal estrogen preparations with the lowest systemic absorption rate may be preferred in women with history of breast cancer and severe vaginal atrophy.[15] No progestin is necessary for endometrial protection, because of the low dosage prescribed for this treatment.[16] DHEA and vaginal testosterone are still in clinical trials, but informal reports from patients has shown these treatments are effective, and there are now health care providers prescribing off-label testosterone in bio-identical drug form.[17]

These treatments are discussed in detail in the resource section of the book's website. Also, this roster of remedies will be kept up to date since new ones are being developed continuously.

Preparation Prior to Sexplay with Anticipated Penetration

It's all about time—creating the time, taking the time, luxuriating in the time. I believe time and timing are essential when deciding to create the pleasures of sexual passion. The time spent in preparation for vaginal penetration prepares your entire body on many levels to envelope your partner's penis. "Time" might be one of the best and hopefully one of the most enjoyable treatments for painful intercourse. Stimulation of the senses takes time, and the more you are stimulated the more aroused you will become. Your once dry vagina might become more lubricated than usual, although it should be noted that even though you are wet your viscosity might have changed and a lubricant may still be a necessary addition. "Time" also is necessary to create a higher level of arousal. This precipitates a process of muscle contractions, which pull the uterus up into the body. This then invites the penis to fill the space comfortably. It also gives your pelvic muscles the opportunity to relax.

Planning the proper environment is especially crucial when you are dealing with the challenges of pain. Have everything you need within easy reach—lube, extra pillows and bolsters, towels, and any devices (aids, toys) you wish to incorporate into your sexplay. Discuss pain issues and possible positions with your partner. (Consult the back pain section below.) This conversation can be done in advance and tweaked if necessary when setting the scene for your sexplay.

Several other measures could help control interruptions such as emptying your bladder, using pain-relieving measures (warm bath or shower and OTC pain relievers or medications) if necessary. Please note that sometimes pain-relieving drugs can interfere with your ability to have an orgasm or it might change the intensity. Apply lidocaine (prescription necessary) or other analgesic to the vaginal opening when and where necessary. Do this after any cunnilingus, but give it enough time to take affect prior to penetration. Lidocaine is extremely effective, but do not apply too much or otherwise you will feel nothing, including the pleasurable sensations. If it rubs off on your husband's penis it can create a numbing sensation for him also, which might make it difficult for him to remain aroused. A little bit goes a long way, so you will have to discover what works best for you both. Using disposable gloves to apply cream, will keep your fingers from becoming numb.

Arousal and orgasm not only bring much pleasure but are also natural pain relievers. Studies have shown that when women have an orgasm their pain tolerance threshold and pain detection threshold increases significantly, by up to 74.6 percent and 106.7 percent respectively.[18] Another study reports that, "sexual activity and orgasm decrease a wide variety of human responses to pain and touch..."[19] Using this information to your advantage, orchestrating a sexual session that begins with an orgasm prior to penetration, which might be to your advantage if you are experiencing pain. Or orgasm with slight penetration, which would then make fuller penetration more comfortable. The position would have to permit the woman to control the depth.

You could experiment using Directed Erotic Visualisation© (DEV©), an immersive audio experience (see preceding chapter) using a blend of meditation, visualization, and suggestion techniques. Women have experienced intense orgasms listening to these audio books. You can experience a hands-free orgasm (HFO), use your fingers or integrate your vibrator/eroscillator when in the throes of one of these stories. Your DEV© listening experience could be done prior to your sex date or you might want to ask your partner to join you. The audio could be used as a trigger to start your process of arousal. If your partner is present, you might just set off an arousal feedback loop.

Nipples and breasts have the capability to arouse,[20] and in some instances women can reach an orgasm while they are being stimulated in those areas.[21] There are even women, like the one who attended the Adult Sex-Ed session of my Erotic Literary Salon, who complain that their nipples are too sensitive. If my attendee's partner tried to touch them, her reflexes took over and she would automatically slap his hand away. I suggested she ask her partner to stimulate other parts of her body first, through kissing, body stroking, and whatever felt comfortable, before allowing him to slowly start caressing her breasts and then begin to stimulate her nipples. At the height of clitoral orgasm some women encourage extreme pinching or biting of nipples. It can develop into a simultaneous genital/nipple orgasm.

Consider having nipple orgasms if you suffer from genital pain. If your nipples are not sensitive, use the information in Chapter 3, Creating Erogenous Zones, to alter your nipple responses. Find positions that will allow for clitoral stimulation and/or nipple stimulation, while your partner's penis enters and strokes the inside of your vagina. This can be another method for increasing your pain threshold.

Sex Positions for the Inflexible, Fragile, and/or Challenged Body

Hidden body pains keep many women from desiring sex— specifically intercourse, because often such pain has more to do with the fear of creating more pain. Earlier in the chapter, I mention how orgasm can help alleviate pain. Below are more suggestions that will aid you in enjoying sex without unintended consequences of pain.

Sharing your hidden disabilities is the first step in creating sexual comfort. Discuss your pain in detail and how it has led you to avoid intercourse and perhaps intimacy altogether, fearing intercourse will be expected. Perhaps your pains have made you depressed or feeling less than your normal self. Expressing yourself sexually is the last thing on your mind, but you also want to satisfy your partner's needs.

Discuss your physical limitations and how best to be physically intimate without creating more unwanted pain. You can do this by reviewing the following suggestions and discussing with your partner which ones you want to try and which others you believe would not serve you.

To Avoid Generalized Muscle and/or Joint Pain

- Schedule sex after you have had the opportunity to exercise, walk, and be active. But not when you are too tired.
- Prior to having sex, take a bath or sit in a hot tub and have your partner massage you, use a heat pack, or help you with anything you do to ease muscle pain prior to sex.

- Take a mild pain reliever approximately 30 minutes prior to sex, but nothing strong, so as not to mask warning pains.
- Use padded furniture and pillows for support (Specially designed sex furniture/wedges are listed on the book's website.)

To Avoid Back Pain

- Use more hip and knee motion than spine movement.
- Try having sex while your husband is seated on a chair and you are sitting on top, either facing him or away. Your feet must be comfortably placed on the ground.
- If your back pain is made worse by arching your back or lying on your stomach, use a modified missionary position with a pillow under your lower back or rear-end.
- If your back pain is heightened by touching your toes or sitting for long periods of time, try spooning or "doggy style." Supporting your upper body with your hands, not your elbows, or with pillows.
- If a hard surface feels better than a mattress, put a blanket or quilt on the floor and then lie on that for your sexplay.

Hip and Knee Replacement

With the continuous changes in hip and knee replacement surgeries, it is difficult to suggest positions. Consult with your physician; ask if it is safe for you to have penetrative sex. This is a conversation to have after being weaned of your walker. If you are still relying on one, it is an indicator that your strength and balance are still being compromised. I suggest you visit the book's website for up-to-date hip and knee replacement sex positions.

Sex with Prolapsed Organs

- Modified version of the missionary position: Lie on your back with pillows under your pelvis to tilt your body so that your prolapse will retract away from your vaginal opening.

- Positions to avoid: Standing up, and with the man lying down and woman on top.

Bladder Conditions: Interstitial cystitis, painful bladder syndrome, urge incontinence.

- Modified version of the missionary position: Place pillow underneath your lower back, which repositions your bladder.

- Avoid "doggy style."

- Intercourse with catheter: Seal it off or remove temporarily. Consult with your physician to reduce fluid intake. If you cannot remove or seal off catheter, tape the tube and bag to your inner thigh or use a long extension tube to place it out of sight.

- Sex position with catheter: Lie on your side with your partner either behind you or on top. Tape the tube and bag to the leg lying on the bed.

Please try the various recommendations I have suggested until you find the ones that work for you. Keep in mind that your body is continually changing, and what might have worked last week, or even yesterday, might not be a good fit today. This means that the conversation regarding the most comfortable sex position with your partner might need to be modified before or maybe even during sexplay.

In this chapter, I have introduced both hidden and overt physical challenges brought on by vaginal wall and pelvic floor changes. Various symptoms have been listed, along with natural and medicinal remedies. Specific techniques and positions have been explained that avoid or lessen unintended pain during sexual expression.

Chapter 6 applies the Ageless Sex philosophy to expanding the physical expression of intimacy. I introduce various forms of non-traditional sex and sex aids, along with exercises to enhance communication during sex.

Chapter 5: Important Points

- Hormonal alteration can result in various physical, psychological, and sexual changes in menopausal women.
- Genitourinary syndrome of menopause (GSM), formerly known as vulvovaginal atrophy and atrophic vaginitis, describes various menopausal symptoms and signs associated with physical changes of the vulva, vagina, and lower urinary tract.
- GSM is a chronic condition with significant impact on sexual health and quality of life. Effective and safe treatment may be available for various symptoms.
- Any change of the pelvic floor muscles, brought on by estrogen depletion, can be painful in and of itself and can affect the health of the vaginal wall.
- Addressing both the physiological and psychological aspects of pain is integral to treatment.
- Pelvic floor disorders can affect the position of the pelvic organs.
- Vulva/vaginal pain that is not related to GSM or other specific disorders is referred to as vulvodynia (unprovoked pain).
- Vestibulodynia (provoked pain) formerly known as vestibulitis, is pain that usually occurs at the bottom section of the vulva, at the opening of the vagina.
- Lichen sclerosus, a commonly overlooked dermatosis, is an autoimmune disorder that presents as white patches, scars, and adhesions on the labia.
- Chronic Pelvic Pain (CPP) syndrome is a pain that lasts more than six months and often overshadows the problem that originally caused the pain.
- Various home remedies and medical treatments can address some of the symptoms related to GSM and vulvodynia.
- Preparation for anticipated penetration is important for controlling or dissipating pain.
- To provide comfort during sexplay, allow time for arousal and for creating a proper environment.
- Directed Erotic Visualisation© (DEV©) is an immersive audio experience, using a blend of meditation, visualization, and suggestion techniques to create a hands-free orgasm (HFO).
- Orgasms can be used to decrease sensitivity to pain.

- Nipples and breasts have the capability to arouse, and some women can reach orgasm through nipple stimulation.
- Specific positions can be used to alleviate pain during a sexual session.

6

EXPANDING THE MENU OF PHYSICAL INTIMACY

A couple's sexual repertoire is usually made up of sexual behaviors they are most comfortable expressing, although often these behaviors have a shelf life. Since it is difficult to remain engaged if boredom sets in as it frequently does with monotony, such boredom plus physical challenges can demand alterations to your usual forms of having sex. Either reason can require changes if you are to enjoy sexual pleasures.

Often my clients complain that their physical problems are interfering with their typical style of expressing themselves sexually. I ask them to take this opportunity of discontent and use it to expand their sexual repertoire, exploring the many forms of sexplay that lead to sexual pleasure while involving no goals or expectations.

Sexplay

"Sexplay" is the term many sexologists prefer to substitute for "foreplay," since it doesn't imply anything more than having fun sexually. There are no expectations of orgasm or intercourse, no anticipation of one action following another, no assumed reciprocation. It is all about play. I end my workshops and lectures with a mission statement: "Think of your bed as a sandbox without the sand, a place to frolic and create much pleasure." I am often approached after my talks by people who had never thought of sex as fun. They appreciate my "assignment," giving them permission to be playful and to relish the pleasure of sex.

Outercourse

Outercourse refers to non-penetrative sex, the type of stimulation that excludes intercourse but can include orgasm. Here's renowned sex therapist Marty Klein's concept of outercourse:

> Outercourse involves a vision of your own eroticism that you design and control. This erotic vision is not subject to the whims of biology, aging, or social custom. It isn't static; you can alter it as you mature, change partners, cope with physical limitations, or grapple with life issues like boredom, fear of aging, and the empty-nest syndrome.

> This outercourse vision has a radical absence of rules (other than consent, honesty, and responsibility): about how bodies should function, about who does what, about how long you should spend doing various activities, about what anything "means."[1]

Think back to your younger years when sex only meant outercourse, and even that form of sex was sinful. Outercourse were those acts of groping that steamed up your family car windows and occasionally left stains on your clothing. Occasionally you might have gone further and included oral sex (cunnilingus and fellatio techniques are described in detail at the book's website). It is a form of expression I recommend to couples when intercourse is painful for the woman or impossible for her husband, or when a couple just wants to change it up. Boredom can zap the erotic energy out of any relationship.

The following case is a composite of numerous heartbroken couples who have found their way to my office, when one member of the dyad is sexually frustrated and the other is in physical and/or emotional pain. As a couple, they have often lost patience with each other and sometimes even lost hope for the relationship, until they realize a sexologist might be the appropriate person to offer guidance.

Initially Betsy did not come willingly to see me, but her husband Ted heard my lecture on *Ageless Sex* and felt that this was exactly what their marriage needed. But having sex was the last thing on Betsy's mind. She recalled complaining about getting hot flashes to her mom, who remarked, "Honeybunch, you can finally stop doing the deed. You're entering menopause, no need to continue pleasing him." At 60, Betsy thought sex was behind her since that was what she was led to believe not only by her mother, but by the other women she overheard at church functions. So she just stopped when it became painful, reinforcing what she had been lead to believe.

As I took Betsy's sexual history, it became apparent that she needed a thorough physical exam plus an evaluation of her genital health before we continued to work together. It was important to find out the origin of her pain so it could be treated appropriately. Once pain free, she could focus on creating her *Authentic Sex Life.*

Betsy's pain issues were related to GSM so her doctor first suggested she try the least invasive remedy: bi-weekly moisturizer treatments plus lubrication prior to vaginal intercourse. This proved insufficient, and a small amount of bio-identical topical estrogen was added. The combination of ointments relieved her pain, but she still didn't feel very motivated to have sex, "just to please" as she stated early on during our sessions. Then she disclosed that she never had orgasms with intercourse, and I encouraged her to discover her *Personal Path to Pleasure.*

We went through the exercises on body imagery, masturbation, communication, shame, and the sexual bucket list as set forth earlier in this book. This created a solid foundation for Betsy to explore various techniques that would expand her sexual repertoire, always keeping in mind the underlying philosophy of the *Ageless Sex Life*: the physical expression of intimacy taking into consideration emotional needs, aging bodies, health challenges, and one's *Conscious Coupling* lifestyle.

As we progressed with her "homework" assignments, she learned that approximately 50% of women report an orgasm with just vaginal intercourse, 71% have an orgasm with hand massage plus intercourse, and 86% have an orgasm following some combination of hand massage, cunnilingus, and intercourse.[2] This information made her realize she needed to change her style of sexplay if orgasm was to be on her agenda.

Betsy asked her husband for support in her adventure to discover new techniques and scenarios for pleasure. She reported Ted was all smiles, but neither one of them expected kissing to be the first behavior on the list. "We do this daily—how can this possibly expand our sex life?" was Betsy's retort when I mentioned kissing. I realize it is a behavior that many couples overlook, and yet it fits into all the categories of the *Personal Path to Pleasure* model, especially as a trigger for sexual expression. As mentioned in Chapter 4, kissing has the power to ignite, but I feel the need to mention it again—it is *that* important. Kissing with intent, a make-out session to arouse, is very different than the kisses we blow in the air or by briskly touching lips as a salutation. The following points are suggestions meant to spur your imagination and then to put your own "spin" on them.

- Spend an extended period of time gazing and kissing.

- Explore each other's mouth with your tongue.

- Play, have fun, laugh, hum while kissing, do something different with each kiss.

- Create passionate noises while kissing.

- Teeny tiny pecks to the other end of the spectrum—swallowing each other's tongue and everything in between.

- Hands to caress only above the shoulders.

- If your eyes are comfortable, try gazing while kissing, or gaze between kisses. Alternate with closed eyes, focusing inward on the aromas and sensation of the kiss.

- When your lips tire, use them to kiss elsewhere above the shoulders—neck, face, scalp.

- Kiss as if you are trying to give each other the most pleasurable experience possible.

- Kiss with no expectation of more, kiss and do nothing but kiss, leave each other panting, wanting for more, until the next time.

- Suck gently on your partners upper or lower lip.

- Gently suck your partner's tongue into your mouth.

I suggested Betsy and Ted consider stepping backwards in time, to their memories of pre-intercourse days. They had not known each other then, since this was their second marriage. Betsy told me, "I held on to my virginity a lot longer than my girlfriends, being raised in a very religious household where sex was considered sinful. What a joke, since I did everything but 'the deed.'" I asked Betsy to recall some of those pre-"deed" sessions with her boyfriends. "I always liked when my boyfriends played with my breasts—they were so tiny then, and my boyfriends made me feel as if they were beautiful.... I had some of my most wonderful make-out sessions experimenting with my best girlfriend. We kissed and felt each other up, got really wet and excited and then stopped. We giggled a lot and had great fun." I suggested she and Ted share their experiences and then role-play as new teenage lovers, sneaking kisses in public, making out on a park bench or on a blanket in the woods. Over a period of several sessions Betsy noted, "We always start outdoors, then work our way to a private spot indoors. We have decided not to assume we are going to have intercourse, but when we do I seem to be ready. I think the time we take making out really gets me prepared." And she is so right; you don't have to wait for bed to start preparing. If your erotic energy is being stimulated throughout the day, it is easier to produce the wanting of sex. You are not starting from ground zero.

I encouraged Betsy and Ted to draw up a list of behaviors they recalled from younger years, and ones they enjoyed as they dated (between previous marriages). They had great fun remembering them and even more fun reenacting them. Here's their list:

- No intercourse.
- Initially clothes stay on, then all clothes off.
- Sometimes words, other times sounds or silence.
- Kissing, especially the ears. Tracing the folds with the tip of the tongue.
- Stroking, cupping, kissing breasts over clothing then place hands underclothing, but over bra if one is worn, then under bra (closure might need to be opened for comfort, but not removed).
- Press hands over inner thighs, then over penis, squeeze and release, stroke. Do the same with testicles—most gently, please.

- Cupping genitals (vulva), alternate pressing fingers, press and stroke clit through clothing.
- Pinch and grope each other's buttocks.
- Rubbing crotches with clothes on.

You can choose to copy some of their behaviors, but I also encourage you to create ones of your own. Some work well in public; others are clearly meant for a private space.

After Betsy and Ted started on their journey to expand their sexual repertoire and pleasure, Betsy realized how much fun sex could be. As sexual pleasure became a part of her life, she found that being 60 was not the final act of sex but the start of her sexual journey towards an *Authentic Sex Life*.

Expanded Sex

Expanded Sex involves the entire body in the act of sexual pleasuring, not just a focus on genital stimulation. It is easy to be genitally focused when trying to enhance sensations, since the clitoris has 8,000 nerve endings. But being sexual with your partner can be more than just having the tip of your clit rubbed and your vagina penetrated. It is about awakening your entire body to intense sensual pleasures, the kind of ecstasy that has many an atheist invoking the words, "Oh God!" in the height of pleasure.

My client Tina had lost interest in sex when her husband Lance could no longer get an erection. He was not interested in taking any drugs or using devices that could potentially get him hard. Her pleasure in sex was equated with a filled vagina, and that was gone. He too lost an interest in sex because he equated orgasm with a hard penis.

When Tina first contacted me, she and her husband had not been physically intimate for several years, nor had they spoken about it. Time passed with little more than perfunctory kisses and quick hugs on a daily basis. It didn't seem to affect their relationship, since neither one missed being sexual and they continued relating as if nothing had changed. Then Tina attended a meeting of her woman's club, where I happened to be the speaker of the month. Later, she told me that she hadn't realized how much she missed sex until I spoke to the group about enjoying sex with a soft penis.

Initially we discussed her situation and sexual goals. I suggested she proceed slowly, since a man with a fickle or soft penis often feels as if he has been robbed of his manhood. We worked out several assignments that would ultimately get them both interested in sex again.

They enjoyed watching movies together, so with much care Tina intentionally chose one with some steamy scenes. She snuggled close to her Lance, something they hadn't done in a long while, but he didn't seem to mind. When the movie ended and she turned on the lights, she began to gaze into his eyes—an important aspect of the exercise. She said at first he balked: "What are you doing, woman?" but with a sweet voice she said, "I haven't looked at your beautiful eyes in a really long while." Which was true. Lance had no choice but to look back, and the intense gaze started to work its magic. After a few minutes she started to stroke his arms and again he drew back, but she continued. She said that it had been obvious he was getting agitated but she continued with kind words, "I miss touching your soft skin and being held by you. I really want the great loving we used to have." And then something unexpected happened: she hit a nerve with her words, and he pulled her close." She was surprised it was this easy after so many years being touched deprived, and she continued the scene.

Lance later mentioned that the words "being wanted" were ones that woke him up. She had never expressed herself like that before, but simultaneously he felt he couldn't please her. So he pulled away yet kept hanging on with his hands. Tina remembered that he said, "I love you, but you know my dick isn't working any longer." And that is when she confessed she had been consulting with me and what she had learned. Tina and I had role-played about how best to talk about her visits with me. and since she mentioned I was a "sex expert," he listened and learned. And he even joined in the sessions to have some of his questions answered.

I had Tina and Lance explore their likes and dislikes, motivations, shared fantasies, many of the same exercises I presented in the beginning of this book. This gave them enough information and a format to create a *Conscious Coupling*. I expressly told them to proceed slowly in discovering new ways of pleasuring each other. When the last session was held, it confirmed why I love my work. Lance spoke first,

"Doc, I'll be the first to admit when Tina talked about you I thought she must be kidding—a sexologist! Never heard that word before. You helped me have the best orgasms without a hard cock, who knew? And I love pleasing my wife." As he said "wife," Tina grabbed Lance's hand and gazed into his eyes, "I love you honey, I hope you never get hard again." And then they broke into sidesplitting laughter. They are no longer my clients, but occasionally I receive emails with some new sexual behavior they discovered.

You can use the following example to open a discussion about your partner's soft cock (with your own words and at the appropriate time).

> You: I love your dick (or nickname) hard or soft, honestly. And I've learned some techniques that will give a soft cock much pleasure. Even orgasm.
> Partner: Seriously!? But I can't ejaculate.
> You: I learned having an orgasm and ejaculating are two different processes.
> Partner: Did you learn that from the book your reading?
> You: Yes, and it even has instructions how to give you an orgasm with your cock remaining soft.

The following points are what Tina and Lance took away from their sessions with me:

- Men can still have an orgasm even though their cocks might not get hard.
- Prostates are still sensitive, even with a soft penis. They can be stimulated by internal or external massage. (See section below on how to "milk" the prostate.) Stimulating the prostate can induce a man to have an intense orgasm.
- Men can use a strap-on cock to fill their partner's vagina.
- Men can hold a dildo in his partner's vagina and stimulate the clitoris with his finger, tongue, vibrator, or whatever part of the body or device feels comfortable. Or his partner could stimulate her own clitoris.

Awakening a Limp Penis: How to Massage the Prostate

You can perform a prostate massage on your partner, internally or externally, but it is essential to remember to communicate during the entire process. Your partner might wish to do this procedure on himself first, or prefer only to do this by himself. In either case the instructions are basically the same.

At no time is this supposed to be painful—pain is a sign of muscles not being prepared properly. Muscles must be relaxed in order to massage the P-spot internally, and this takes time and a lot of trust in your partner. Charlie Glickman, PhD, coauthor with Aislinn Emirzian of *The Ultimate Guide to Prostate Pleasure: Erotic Exploration for Men and Their Partners*, made an interesting observation: "Doctors are trained to not make prostate exams feel good, because they don't want to be accused of sexual harassment. So don't let your experiences with a doctor get in your way of enjoying yourself."[3]

Internally: The internal prostate massage instructions are worded for self-massage. Comments in parenthesis are added to some sentences to add instructions for partner. Note: Do not proceed if you have any prostate issues; consult with your physician first.

Tools

- Time: I consider this a tool; although not a device, it is an extremely important ingredient in the making of a powerful P-spot orgasm. Probably not less than one hour.
- Do whatever works for you to place yourself in a calm state; meditate, warm shower/bath, etc.
- Create an environment to promote comfort: soothing music or none, ringers off, doors closed/locked, implements nearby, including towel, lubricant, and toy/aid if you are to use one.
- Massager: finger (trimmed nails and clean hands) or prostate toy/aid
- Lubricant (silicone oil should not be used with silicone toy): use any good over the counter anal lube. DO NOT use any numbing creams because then you won't know if it is hurting, and afterwards you will suffer. Avoid products with scents or

dyes as part of the ingredients. Experiment. Purchase small/sample sized bottles of lube until you find one you really like.

- Gloves: highly recommended, (choose wisely if you are latex sensitive). Clean your rectum. Either use a tiny medicated enema from the drug store (empty the bottle and fill with water) or insert your finger to remove any lodged feces after defecating. This can be done in the toilet or shower.

- Apply lubricant to finger in preparation for finger entry, which will help open the anal muscle. This entire process, detailed below, is done in slow motion. Do not hold your breath. (Occasionally check if your partner is holding their breath. Ask him to slowly take a deep breath and then to keep on breathing naturally.)
    - o Use tip or pad of finger/thumb to gently stimulate the anus. Use various light strokes and rubbing with one or more fingers, then thumbs, and work around than across the opening. Play with different motions and see which massage feels best.
    - o When the anus seems to respond by twitching, even if it is only a teeny amount, you might be ready to proceed.
    - o Hold the pad of your finger over the anus for 5-10 seconds and when you feel the <u>external</u> sphincter muscle soften slowly, ever so slowly proceed to slide it in up to the first finger joint. Sometimes if the muscles are extremely relaxed, your finger will feel pulled in and there is no need to stop.
    - o Then proceed to relax the <u>internal</u> anal sphincter muscle (it will feel like a tight ring inside) by tickling it with your fingertip. It might take up to a minute to open; if your uncomfortable, slowly withdraw your finger and start from the beginning. At this point the anus might respond faster, and you can enter again and try to relax the inner muscle.

- o Some men enjoy stroking their penis simultaneously, but others find it distracting. The only problem with stroking the penis: you might orgasm, and this will make it difficult to have a prostate orgasm. One suggestion would be to stroke the penis gently until the internal anal sphincter muscles have relaxed and then stop.

- You are now ready to locate the prostate gland (P-spot), which is approximately 3-4" in from the anus and about 1" across. (See diagram on book's website.) Curl your finger up after entry towards the navel. It usually feels like a hard lump. During arousal it fills with liquid that is released during ejaculation. Once filled, it will feel like a firm plum. If your prostate is difficult to locate, it is likely you need further arousal, so massage yourself or use sensual massages, oral sex, penis stroking, kissing, to name a few arousal behaviors.

- Once you have located the prostate and felt it with your finger, you might feel the need to urinate. If so, apply less pressure. If you know you've found it but you don't feel anything, it might take several anal massage sessions before you can focus on the sensations.

- There are many combinations for creating anal pleasure:
  - o Prostate stimulation with finger(s) or prostate stimulator,* with and without vibrator.
  - o Anal canal stimulation by friction (butt plug—with or without vibrator—which must have a flanged base) using an in and out motion.
  - o Kegel exercises. The man can lift and release the muscles that start and stop the flow of urine while having his P-spot stimulated. He should keep breathing during this process, and at times take deep breaths while tightening the muscle then slowly release the muscle. This exercise allows for the use of a toy, if you and he decide to use one, to be pushed along the rectal wall muscles and eventually hit the prostate.

○ Once your man has achieved a prostate orgasm, he might want to stroke his penis and create another one. He doesn't need a hard penis to have either orgasm. Practicing Kegel exercises will also strengthen the muscles that are used to create the powerful orgasmic sensations.

Externally (Do not proceed if the man has any prostate issues. He should consult his physician first.) This is considered an indirect method of P-spot massage, more difficult but not impossible for inducing a prostate orgasm.

- It is not necessary to prep for anal entry, since this massage is done externally. But do follow directions for creating a calm state.
- This style of P-spot massage will probably take longer, so consider setting aside more time.
- The area to be massaged is located approximately midway along the perineum*, down between the anus (rectal opening) and the scrotum (testicle pouch, or "balls"). There is a raised line of skin running vertically between these points.
- Start massaging using several fingers then knuckles or smooth object. Discover what works best by "playing" with various pressures and movements and directions.
- You can add strokes to the penis, similarly to the external P-spot massage.

Some men prefer to try external prostate massage on themselves to see what feels best. At some point, your partner might invite you to enjoy participating in the process with him. There is a steep learning curve, and it takes time and sometimes much practice to achieve an orgasm. But the process is extremely enjoyable even if no orgasm results.

Role Playing

Why you want to role play may vary, but one aspect of this type of interaction is consistent—the taking on of a different persona. Role playing gives you the opportunity to be someone you emulate, or to express hidden aspects of your personality. In order for role playing to work effectively however, you must be comfortable stepping out of character, responding to life in a different manner. Sometimes the scenes you agree upon with your partner can be quite silly, so you must be willing to act foolishly and sometimes feel awkward. You get to speak, dress, act in a manner that is not always politically correct. It is all about fantasy, but it can also be used to explore sexual behaviors you have been considering but were too bashful to try. With a new persona it is often easier to experiment without feeling embarrassed.

Scenes can be created specifically for the bedroom or staged in public, such as the bar setting in Chapter 4. Below are several examples of characters and scenes. You can also consider switching traditional gender roles.

- Dominant - submissive
- Librarian - patron
- Teacher – student
- Boss – employee
- Older person – child
- Doctor – patient
- House person – delivery person
- Child – babysitter
- Police officer – criminal
- Losing virginity
- Nurse – patient
- Famous person – groupie
- Massage with "happy ending" (orgasm)
- Porn stars making movie
- Prostitute – customer
- Fitness/yoga instructor – client
- Person – vampire
- House person – repair person
- Landlord – tenant
- Casting director - actor
- Driver – mechanic
- Royalty – peasant
- Robot – person
- Stripper – patron

- Driver – hitchhiker
- Disney character – human
- Firefighter – victim being rescued
- Artist – model
- Athlete – cheerleader
- Wedding night
- Reenact movie sex scene
- Dance instructor – student
- Hotel maid – guest
- Maid – homeowner
- Butler - homeowner

The comfort you each feel in creating role play scenes will determine how you proceed. I suggest you try several scenes before deciding whether role playing should be included in your sexual repertoire. If the act of role play turned you *both* off, then check that off your list of "tools." Maybe one of you enjoyed role playing and would really like to create a scene on a regular or occasional basis. You could agree to allow that person to find someone else to create the scene with and bring the excitement of the interaction home, or have the other person watch or in the room for safety (depending upon the scene). For example, if you enjoy being dominated but your husband is not interested in inflicting strong sensations, you could find someone to do what pleases you. (The book's website will give you details on how to locate people who are into the BDSM lifestyle.)

Make certain you discuss boundaries whenever you take a scene outside of your relationship. My client Katie was most distressed because she felt she had to stop seeking scenes. Her husband Jamie became upset at the last one while watching her enjoyment and she loved him too much to ignore his response. I met with both of them, and Katie then learned that Jamie felt her flogger was getting too intimate. He had put his arm around her as he proceeded with the lashings and leaned into her body. Katie's response was interesting. She loved that her husband was jealous, she took it as a sign of love. But for future scenes, they agreed upon limits of touching while she was being flogged.

If BDSM is going to be the type of scene you would like to do together, then follow the guidelines in Chapter 4 for safe words and signals. The book's website has listings of sites and books pertaining to BDSM tutorials. You can also find other styles of fantasy scenes plus sites to purchase paraphernalia to create a scene.

Introducing Tools to Arouse in the Bedroom

I have heard women say that the hardest part of using a sex toy is introducing it to their sex partner. If you have had push-back in the past or are expecting it, find out why your partner is not interested. A typical concern is that the tool, often vibrator, works so well that you will not need him to produce pleasure. Well, we both know that this is hogwash, but you need to convince him. Vibrators don't cuddle, aren't warm and fuzzy, and don't whisper amorous words in your ear. Explain to him this is not an either-or situation, but a tool to enhance pleasure and not to replace him.

Becky was having difficulties creating traditional orgasms, and her frustration level usually had her giving up. Her hand got tired stroking her own genitals or she felt her husband's resignation when he tried it, and it seemed to take forever and then—nothing. She wasn't even enjoying the pleasure of the build-up because she knew in advance she would not feel satisfied. When she approached her husband Ben with the idea of using a vibrator, he felt threatened. He was under the typical male misconception that perhaps he was not good enough, and he would be replaced by a sex toy.

I suggested she visit a sex toy shop together with Ben, and I recommended tools they could use as a couple. These tools make a great "first toy," since they pleasure both partners. New sex toys are constantly being designed and upgraded, so I have included an up-to-date list of toys and online stores on the book's website along with on-line stores.

Devices to Arouse

There are many tools that can be used to create divine sensations of pleasure and enhance blood flow to the genitals, nipples, and any area that arouses you. Some of them are attached to your body—such as fingertips, palms, tip of tongue, breath, and hair, plus others that can be found in cosmetic shops, hardware stores, and sex-toy purveyors.

The typical sex-toy stores carry a variety of sex aids, and you can also find some listed on the book's website. The most widely known tools are wand vibrators, which have large heads and create a throbbing sensation. The lessor known Eroscillator (my go-to favorite), has several attachments to add to the base that moves from side to side rapidly—similar to some electric toothbrushes. The unique design allows you to use it as a self-pleasuring tool or during intercourse.

I suggest you either set up an appointment to be taken through an upscale sex-toy shop (you can judge it by the interior display, lighting and types of sex toys—they are not cheap toys), or ask to speak with a knowledgeable sales associate. Many stores and home party sex-toy companies (listed on the book's website) train their sales force specifically on the needs and desires of older women. You might never have used a sex-aid, making it difficult to know what type would best fit your needs or interest in experimenting. Please don't be shy when speaking with someone at the sex-toy shop; there is always a first time for everything, and the workers at the shop have seen and heard it all.

The broad categories of sex-aids available for both men and women include:

- Vibrators
- Eroscillators
- Pulsators
- Dildos
- Anal aids
- Penis aids
- Nipple clamps
- Kegel exercisers
- Remote control toys
- App-controlled aids (distance play)
- Role play aids
- BDSM paraphernalia
- Lubricants
- Peek-a-boo clothing, cut-out bras, pasties, and other specialty wearables
- Prostate stimulators

- Penis rings
- Vibrating penis rings
- Vacuum penile devices
- Penis sleeves
- Penis extensions

Other than through a sex shop, there are plenty of devices useable for sex that are easily available in various stores. Once I met with a group of women interested in reviving what they considered was a boring sex-life, and I suggested they visit a box hardware store, the kind of shop that seems to have endless supplies of everything to build a house. Their assignment was to walk the aisles with their partner and load a cart with "sex aids." I encouraged them to be inventive and find devices to create a variety of sensations, such as ropes for restraints if they were interested in role-playing with bondage, or just wanting to keep "hands-off" when they are giving pleasure. Pantyhose and soft scarves can also work well for bondage.

A hand-held shower nozzle applied with varying intensities is great when directed towards genitals. Spring-loaded wooden clothespin placed where you would normally like pinches offer powerful sensations. (You are able to loosen springs on some, if it feels too tight.) These are just a few items that are not usually found in sex-toy shops. The hair department in drugs stores offer various kinds of hair clips and clamps that not only hold back hair but work well on nipples and other parts of the body. Ice cubes and chilled metal objects placed on nipples and other parts of the body also create strong sensations.

Sexuality author Jay Wiseman has applied his creative nature to sex advice. It started with gathering "tricks" his sex partners used to improve their sex lives and culminated in his book *Supermarket Tricks: More Than 125 Ways to Improvise Good Sex*. This is a great read if you wish to discover ideas for creating interesting and sometimes intense sensations in bed. The high-end sex shops sell wonderful safe items, but it can be fun traveling through the aisles of other stores finding implements that might create interesting sensations for erotic play.

Gail, a workshop attendee, regaled us with an account of rummaging through her new boyfriend Pete's bathroom drawers looking for a nail file and finding instead a fabric roll filled with dozens of make-up brushes.

> As I kept looking for make-up, thoughts kept running through my mind—did they belong to an old girlfriend or, worse, was he cheating on me? Or were they his? Pete never mentioned acting and being on stage. I was too shy to ask— what if he was a crossdresser? Well, I thought, if he only did it in the bedroom, I could deal with it. I had a boyfriend once who liked playing with my make-up occasionally, but I didn't know how I'd feel if (Pete) did it often. I decided not to say anything because I really liked the guy. Thank goodness I didn't—(I) would have made a fool of myself.

She then went on to say how she found out later that evening what he used them for.

> While I was in bed waiting for him, he rummaged through the drawer next to the bed and what appeared next startled me—blindfolds. "Trust me?" He said. We had been dating for a while, and I really didn't have any reason not to, so I said yes. He placed the blindfolds gently on my face and asked me not to touch him. Then what came next was an even bigger surprise—he began brushing my body—yes, with *those* brushes. When he was finished brushing, I realized how wet I was—down there. He didn't give me the chance to play with him like I usually do to get him hard. He didn't need me to; my response to the brushing turned him on, and he was super hard and had applied lube to his penis, something I usually do. Just as he took off my blindfold he entered me, our eyes locked, we both had loud orgasms and then fell into each other's arms. After a while, he described in great detail the different brushes he used for my different body parts. Just the retelling of this scene got us turned on, so we "made-out" like teenagers and enjoyed cuddling for the rest of the night.

The tension in the air was almost palpable as she recounted her story, explaining in great detail the sensations Pete aroused in her using the different brushes.

Clitoral Stimulators to Enhance Traditional Orgasm

I have singled out the tip, or "glans," of the clitoris for special attention because most women stimulate this area to create traditional clit-centered orgasms. The visibility of the clitoral glans allows for easy access to the 8,000 nerve endings it contains. (This is twice the number found in the glans of a penis.) Actually, the entire clitoral complex is only partially exposed. The tip sits under a hood, which can also be seen, but three-quarters of the full organ is hidden. A detailed illustration can be found on the book's website. The purpose of the hood is to protect the external part of the clit from excessive stimulation, such as clothing rubbing against it or irritants such as some strong soaps.

There is controversy regarding the movement of the hood during arousal. Some experts point to the enlarged glans pushing the hood back, and others mention the ligaments attached to the clitoral glans pulling it back under the hood during arousal. But what is important is that the hood moves. A rigid hood that is attached to the glans could create discomfort, even pain. "Clitoral adhesions may also be associated with decreased sensation, muted orgasms, or dorsal small fiber sensory neuropathy of the clitoris leading to persistent genital arousal disorder."[4] The source of such adhesions could be a build-up of bacteria, skin cells, or dried sebum, which causes sticking and prevents the friction between the hood and the clitoris. This would interfere with the uncovering of the glans for easier access to stimulation and comfortable clitoral arousal. If clitoral adhesions are a problem for you, you can try sitting in warm bath and gently washing the area on a regular basis (use only plain water). If you are not successful in dislodging the adhesion, consult with your physician.

Because this is such a sensitive area of the body, many women complain that it "hurts" or doesn't feel good when they are touched directly on the clit. As with nipple play I suggest getting turned on first by being touched either near the clit or on other areas of the body. Once in a state of arousal, being touched can often be more than tolerated—it is often welcome.

There are various clitoral aids and one prescribed apparatus that are meant to create suction over the clitoris in order to pull blood towards the area. A clitoris becomes enlarged with blood prior to orgasm, and these tools can enhance and/or hasten an orgasm. Some women additionally apply a finger, vibrator, or Eroscillator, to the clit once it is engorged. The prescribed apparatus (EROS Clitoral Therapy Device) is expensive and not covered by health insurance, but for women who are uncomfortable with the thought of using an object purchased in a sex-toy shop, this feels more therapeutic. The brain response is a large part of the orgasm process, so if you don't feel at ease using a particular device, an orgasm is not likely.

The "rabbit" is a G-spot stimulator or vaginal vibrating dildo with an attached clit stimulator. This is an interesting concept, but it will only work if the dildo fits the inner contours of your body. Depending upon the location of your clit in reference to your G-spot and vagina, this could either be a most frustrating experience or create an extraordinary orgasm using only one hand to hold the device.

All clit stimulators are not created equal, thankfully. The intensity and types of vibrations differ, giving women a variety of choices. Unfortunately, when purchasing you can only hear the noise the toy makes and how it feels on exposed parts of your body, such as your arm. But this might not match what your clitoris appreciates and what is needed to create an orgasm. It is why some women admit to having a drawer filled with sex toys, but they definitely have a favorite.

There are also arousing and enhancing lotions that women either love or hate. For women, the tingling or warming sensation created by the application of these lotions to their clitoris or vagina can produce a range of feelings from an unwanted severe burning sensation to pleasurable warmth or tingling. Unfortunately, it can sometimes be difficult to tell if the sensation it has created is having an intended effect or irritating your skin. I suggest treading cautiously and using small amounts at first.

Lubricating the hood and clitoral glans allows you to buffer the stimulation from various vibrating toys. The lubricating substance can also conduct the vibrations and enhance the effect. But if the sensations feel too intense, you can cover your genitals with a towel or cloth. The vulva/vaginal skin responds poorly to certain lubricant ingredients, and these along with listing of lubricants can be found on the book's website. Some sex shops sell samples or small bottles of these lotions to try out before investing in a larger quantity. If a store has a sample bottle to try in-house, I recommend applying a small amount to the inside of your elbow where the skin is quite thin, and see the reaction. You can also find out if the lubricant has a long-lasting effect by placing a drop or two on your thumb and proceed to dab your thumb and first finger together creating a "string" effect with the lubricant. Once it no longer has the "string" between these fingers, the lubricant is no longer effective. Try several different varieties and compare, finding the one that lasts the longest and feels the best.

Sensual Massage

A sensual massage is intended to create pure pleasure for the sake of pleasure, allowing the receiver the opportunity to luxuriate in the touch sensation without expecting any reciprocal action. The massage can cover the entire body or just focus on a particular part of the body, but the purpose is pure pleasure.

The application can be as light as a breath stroke or sharp as an entire hand of fingernails scratching. Instead of hands, you can use a piece of furry material, feather, brush (as noted earlier), massage candle wax (purchased in sex toy shops), anything that creates a sensation when applied to the skin. Even a man's penis/testicles and a woman's vulva can be treated with varying strokes, pinches, and pulling of skin without any sexual intent. The massage can end with nothing more than the pleasure of the massage or it can be part of sexplay used to build up and enhance sexual ecstasy. The book's website has an extensive section on books, websites, and videos that cover sensual massage.

Neo-Tantric Sex

Tantric sex, spiritual sex and sacred sex — as practiced in the West and often called Neo-Tantra — are terms used together or separately to explain a sexual experience "beyond" typical sex. Most of these practices incorporate meditation, special breathing techniques, massage, and focusing on sensations. All of these methods may weave and expand energy to promote intentional connection with one's self and a partner. As my dear friend Anando explained it so succinctly, "It is all about being present." Actually, it is far more involved, but being present is a state I believe everyone should be in whether communicating vertically or horizontally.

Information about these practices, along with course offerings, can be found on the book's website.

Chapter 6 is continued on the book's website, where you will find information and links to vetted sites that focus exclusively on sexual pleasuring and sexual behaviors.

This chapter has focused on expanding the menu of physical intimacy, introducing non-traditional and conventional sex toys and aids.

Chapter 7 addresses medicinal remedies for arousal and libido issues. On the book's website I include more detail and also cover nutritional products that either work directly or indirectly to solve specific sex-related problems.

Chapter 6: Important Points

- Expanding one's sexual repertoire has the potential of relieving boredom in the bedroom and can help a couple deal with physical challenges.
- Sexplay is foreplay with no expectations of an orgasm.
- Think of your bed as a sandbox without the sand, a place to frolic and create much pleasure.
- Outercourse refers to non-penetrative sex, but can include orgasm.
- Kissing and gazing are important physical acts that help with sexual arousal.
- Expanded Sex involves the entire body in the act of sexual pleasuring, not just a focus on genital stimulation.
- The clitoris has 8,000 nerve endings, and when stimulated has the capability to create traditional orgasms.

- Men can orgasm with a soft penis.
- Stimulating the prostate can induce an intense orgasm.
- Introducing sex toys/aids has the potential to enhance sexual pleasure, but does not replace a partner's touch.
- There are numerous tools to create sensations of pleasure and enhance blood flow for arousal.
- Various sex toys/aids are specifically designed to stimulate the clitoris.
- A sensual massage is intended to create pure pleasure for the sake of pleasure.
- Neo-Tantric Sex practices use various techniques and methods that may weave and expand energy to promote intentional connection with one's self and a partner.
- Vetted sites that focus exclusively on sexual pleasuring and sexual behaviors can be found on the book's website.

7

TREATMENTS FOR AROUSAL AND LIBIDO ISSUES

My views on remedies for arousal and libido issues were discussed briefly in the introduction. Since I use a holistic approach, I am most concerned with the proper diagnosis, which is absolutely necessary for the best outcome. Oftentimes there are several treatments available, and the choice is dependent upon your view of menopause and the practitioner you consult.

The vaginal changes brought on by hormone imbalance tend to initiate a domino effect, which is often the culprit behind many women ultimately self-defining their issue as *low libido*. Consider viewing your vaginal skin as an equivalent to your face —they both alter with age.

The face is impacted most by hereditary factors that are uncontrollable. Then there are the controllable factors, which are usually the result of exposure to environmental hazards. For example, sunlight can cause loss of elasticity, cancerous and noncancerous skin growths, pigment changes, and thickening of the skin. Plus, there are other causes of skin changes. Skin disorders are common among older people since they are more likely to have conditions such as obesity, nutritional deficiencies, diabetes, blood vessel diseases, heart and liver problems, and stress. These all impact the skin negatively. Since so many older people suffer from these conditions, it confuses people into thinking that the resulting skin changes are a natural part of the aging process, independent of other medical problems.

The appearance of our facial skin affects our self-image, but it can also indicate fragile skin, which increases the risk of skin injury. Various over-the-counter creams and lotions can protect the skin (sunscreens and moisturizers are most commonly used), and sometimes prescription drugs. Different treatments are used to deal with severe medical problems, while other therapies (plastic surgery) focus on appearance.

The condition of the vagina changes as we age, also, specifically due to the major impact hormone imbalance has on the vaginal/vulva skin. There are many disorders that occur because of these changes as we age, so these disorders can also be viewed as part of the natural aging process. However, the thinning of the skin can be considered dangerous, since it increases the risk of infection. Treating thinning of the vulva/vaginal skin is similar to treating the face, with creams and lotions—specifically, lubricants and moisturizers. Some over-the-counter and others by prescription (including hormones) are used to prevent or alleviate this problem.

Some women consider facial skin changes a natural part of their own aging, viewing their appearance as matching their chronological age and not particularly bothered by the changes in their looks. But they are willing to use measures to prevent damage caused by environmental conditions that could have significant negative impact on future health.

I suggest you consider your vagina/vulva area in a similar fashion. Here, too, thinning of skin can lead to tears and infections—leading in turn to pain and threats to health, whether you intend to activate your sex drive or not. Whether you are suffering already or have not felt the impact of hormone imbalance, view the various treatments on the book's website. (I have deliberately placed information about specific treatments on the website to keep the information up to date.) Then discuss your concerns and available treatments with your sexual health provider. Do not be surprised if they have not heard of all the remedies you research on the site. And perhaps your practitioner can offer others that are not listed on the site. (Please make suggestions on the website for new available products.) Included among the western treatments are ones that have their roots in eastern medicine and philosophy.

Mindfulness meditation is one practice that has proven to significantly enhance attention to sexual stimuli,[1] sexual desire, sexual arousal, lubrication, sexual satisfaction, reduction in depressive symptoms and overall sexual functioning.[2] It is also one of the least invasive treatments with no negative side effects. (There has been no evidence to date that low-intensity mindfulness meditation causes harm.) The goal of this style of meditation is to exercise the mind to pay attention more fully and without judgement. This will ultimately lead to being in more control of your choices and responses.

Once you learn how to practice mindfulness meditation, you can then specifically focus on areas of your body that bring you pain or discomfort, or that need to be consciously noticed. When you notice the congestion and engorgement of your vaginal walls, you can then translate that feeling into a sexual trigger. (Various meditation tutorials are listed on this book's website.)

Acupuncture also has been used effectively in the treatment of vulvodynia,[3] as well as to enhance libido, lubrication,[4] and sexual desire.[5] I suggest you find a certified and preferably recommended acupuncturist and be honest regarding your issues. You might have to try a few different practitioners before you feel results. If after several sessions you feel no difference, then I would suggest you try a different modality. (Note—acupuncture needles are extremely thin; you can barely feel them entering.)

Yoga has the potential to significantly improve desire, arousal, lubrication, orgasm, and satisfaction, and also to alleviate pain according to a study of women enrolled in a yoga camp.[6] Another study examined a small sample enrolled in a group-based therapeutic yoga program for women with chronic pelvic pain (CPP). Researchers noticed a substantial decrease in these women's subjective pain.[7] There is also much anecdotal evidence available in various lay publications and websites that support these findings.

I have deliberately placed treatments on the book's website to keep the information up to date. Discuss your concerns and available treatments with your sexual health provider. Do not be surprised if they have not heard of all the remedies you research on the site and perhaps they have others that are not listed on the site.

Chapter 8 offers alternative relationship styles to maintain an intimate connection when partners have widely varied sexual needs.

Chapter 7: Important Points

- Proper diagnoses of libido and arousal issues are necessary for the best outcome.
- Treatment choices are dependent upon your view of menopause and the approach of the health care provider you choose.
- Up-to-date vaginal health treatments and lotions can be found on the book's website.
- Eastern medical and philosophical practices may be useful in alleviating pain and enhancing pleasure.

8

HOW TO HONOR EVERYONE'S SEXUAL NEEDS

You have read through the book, followed the directions you have chosen as best for you, consulted with your health care practitioner and for some a therapist, and concluded:

- You are interested in reviving your sex life.
  Or:
- You are interested in being sexual but not as often or using a different style as your partner. (See examples, coming up.)
  Or:
- You have no interest in being sexual but would like to remain in your relationship.

Whichever conclusion you have chosen, following the principle of *Conscious Coupling* will ensure that you and your partner both can live your *Authentic Sex Life* and have your sexual needs met.

Married Several Times...to the Same Person

If you have been married for enough years that you have watched each other grow emotionally, perhaps raised children together, weathered many storms, and now feel like you are dealing with another turbulence—a sexual one—you might want to think of each phase as a separate marriage with the same person. Tammy Nelson, sexologist and sex therapist, coined the phrase *new monogamy*, a model she developed to help her clients revive their marriage while dealing with infidelity:

> The new monogamy can be described as the conscious choices a couple makes about their sexual and emotional fidelity when they both agree to stay together and make it work. The new monogamy also means that each marriage is highly individualized. Partners have the right to make any agreement they want that works for both of them concerning what their monogamy will look like…. It could mean making agreements that aren't considered acceptable in most marriage traditions. In the new monogamy, both partners get to agree on what their relationship will look like, based solely on their shared needs, expectations, and desires.[1]

Your relationship might not be feeling the strains of infidelity, but if there is unresolved desire discrepancy, then cheating or even divorce is not an unusual outcome if your partner is trying to get his sexual needs met.

Whether you have decided to make an erotic connection part of your marriage or remain a sexless couple, a revision of your original vows is essential for navigating your decision. Living with a conscious coupling agreement will help you navigate how you express your intimate connection.

Conscious Coupling Agreement

It would not be unusual to wonder what your marriage is based on if you are no longer monogamous. Traditional monogamy is about being sexual and/or emotionally involved with only one partner. By contrast, consensual non-monogamy (CNM)* is an umbrella term that refers to various styles couples navigate consensually that gives them the option to have one or more additional sexual and/or emotional arrangements. Some of these styles include:

- Polyamory*
- Swinging*
- Monogamish*
- Open Relationship*

- Designer Relationship*
- New Monogamy
- *Conscious Coupling*

With the *Conscious Coupling* model, your commitment is focused on making certain both of your needs are met. This model will also allow you the flexibility to think outside of the traditional monogamy paradigm in order to help your coupledom thrive.

Most people get married with little thought to sexual commitment because it is understood to be the backbone of a traditional marriage. It also tends to be cut in stone, with no allowance for change. I was having an exchange with the newly engaged Pete and Maria when I posed the question, "Have you discussed monogamy?" Pete immediately said, "No we don't have to—marriage means having sex only with each other." Maria chimed in, "if Peter ever cheated on me I would divorce him immediately, no questions asked." I then countered, "Which means you are asking him to lie if he has a one-night stand. If he doesn't get caught or says "no" when he's confronted, you will still remain married. But if you find out, you divorce him." I suggested that they have a discussion about monogamy before marrying, and to design an agreement which has the flexibility to change as they and their marriage develop.

Conscious Coupling agreements should have few set rules other than making certain it is a flexible and a negotiable agreement. Plus, your commitment must take into consideration what each of you desires and expects of the sexual expression of your intimate relationship, and allow for reevaluation on a regular basis.

Negotiating a Non-Traditional Commitment

Now the best part begins: you get to collaborate as a couple to fulfill the sexual desires of both of you. I suggest working backwards and decide how you each envision your new relationship/marriage/phase. (If you could wave a magic wand...) Consider an ideal relationship, not what you think is possible based on your past conversations and experience with your partner. Try to envision your relationship as not influenced by the opinions of friends, family, and society in general. Do this part of the exercise separately so you don't even feel guided by each other's thoughts. Come to your negotiating table with your personal agreement plan, and see where you match and where a negotiation is needed.

Use the collaborative negotiating style (win/win) to make certain you both have your needs met. Work on one issue at a time, and at the end view the agreement as a whole and make certain you walk away with the feeling that you both have won. Important points to keep in mind when negotiating a win/win solution:

- Consider what outcome would make you personally feel you have won—that is, the bottom line. The relationship framework for the final agreement might not be your initial ideal one, but you would still feel your needs are being met.
- Make certain your issues and desires are understood. If you are not sure, have your partner verbally mirror your concerns and requests back to you.
- When you are feeling discouraged with negotiations, point out areas of agreement. This will help focus on the positive and reinforce why you are continuing the process.
- If at an impasse:
  o Reframe your words or ask your partner to reframe his. For example, talk about reasons why your request is important to you, how it would make you feel if it wasn't met, and how your partner's request makes you feel. Ask his opinion at all times, and offer yours.
  o Break down the specific issue into smaller concerns.
  o Try to find areas of agreement within each issue if possible.
  o Think outside of the box to find innovative and alternative solutions, not necessarily ones imposed by society.

If you feel stuck, I suggest you consult with a third party (therapist or counselor who is or would be comfortable with non-traditional marriage agreements); they will be helpful in facilitating the process. The following examples show long-term couples with various sexual needs, and how they have redefined their relationship using the *Conscious Coupling* model.

Becky and Bruce had been married for thirty plus years, and the last ten had been officially sexless. After attending one of my workshops, Becky decided to approach her husband with the idea of consulting with me privately as a couple. At the first session, she confessed what sex was like before she took my workshop. Bruce's face expressed his shock at hearing her words, since she had never confided in him about her medical issues:

> I did my duty so Bruce wouldn't bother me for another month, and between "duty" days I usually itched like crazy. Every doctor I saw said the same thing: "You must have a yeast infection." I assumed they knew what they were talking about, since it was their automatic response without even testing my vaginal fluids. But the creams they gave me never seemed to work for long; every time I had intercourse, the same thing happened. I would itch like crazy.
>
> I was ranting one day to my good friend Rosemary, describing why I hated sex. She said I must make an appointment with her gynecologist because he was the best. I figured I had nothing to lose but a few more dollars wasted if I was told again that I had a yeast infection.
>
> But to my surprise he looked and said he needed to do a biopsy to confirm his suspicion, and he was right. I have lichen sclerosus (LS),* a skin condition he said that often occurs in post-menopausal women, and that I need to treat it for the rest of my life. Strange that I felt happy when he told me that, but it meant it wasn't in my head, which some doctors had me believing.

Once Becky had her flare-ups under control with the proper medication, she again was able to have intercourse comfortably. But then she realized that even with medication, her desire for sexual expression was very different than her husband's. That is when Becky decided to take my workshop and brought the worksheets home.

Together they followed my guidelines and figured out their individual *Authentic Sex Life*. But they were at an impasse trying to have their needs met. I introduced the idea of expanding their monogamous relationship and using the points mentioned earlier in this chapter to create a conscious couple agreement. To my surprise Becky was all ears but Bruce resisted.

> Bruce: I can't imagine Becky in the arms of another man—she's mine.
> Becky: What do you mean—mine? You don't possess me.
> Bruce: Well I'm not going to share you with another man.
> Becky: What are you afraid of? I'm going to run off with someone else?

After much discussion and disclosure, Bruce's beliefs were laid bare. He realized that he felt being married to Becky meant possessing all of her. Becky made it quite clear she was not interested in running off with another man and in fact wanted to explore being physical with women also. She assured Bruce she loved him and only wanted for his happiness, but did not want to feel like she was his possession.

I asked them to discuss their ideal relationship:

Becky: I would like a weekly date night with Bruce, one where we plan something special and intentionally try to turn each other on before we go to bed. But I only want intercourse once a month. I want one day a week to spend with special friends and permission to be intimate with them.

Bruce: I want sex with Becky weekly and to incorporate kink. When Becky goes out with her friends once a week, I want permission to frequent a strip club or *dungeon**, which I enjoyed before we got married. I gave it up to remain faithful to her.

Negotiating their agreement meant first figuring out the obstacles to changing their relationship model. Their beliefs were explored using the option dialogue model, and it became evident that Becky was still fearful of intercourse pain. For his part, Bruce really wanted kink to be part of their lives. It was decided that they would start with monthly intercourse, and if Becky felt comfortable she would let Bruce know if she wanted more. She also made it clear that when they did plan to have intercourse they would have to spend extra time preparing. With LS, she needed a lot of foreplay and lots of lube.

They talked about the type of kink that interested Bruce, and Becky was willing to do light bondage and submission play, definitely nothing that would leave marks on her body. Bruce asked if she would join him at a dungeon but only to watch, and Becky said she would go once and perhaps more if it didn't turn her off. They decided not to add any other details or rules at this time.

As with all these agreements, they needed to be flexible and honor each other's desires. This allows couples to relate comfortably, knowing they share the same goal of maintaining a *Conscious Coupling*.

Greg and Marian were another long-term couple who shared the same household for almost twenty-five years. When Marian first came to see me, I suggested she visit her physician and inquire about using a different antidepressant. The one she was initially prescribed affected her sex drive negatively. Once a new antidepressant was found with fewer side effects, her sex drive was revived. She now focused her erotic energy on Greg who admitted he had been satisfying himself with online porn and wasn't interested in stopping. That is when Marian suggested they consult with a health professional because she was certain that one would agree with her and ask Greg to stop. The Internet led them to me and after hearing their story, I suggested creating a *Conscious Coupling* agreement. They each expressed their ideal relationship, along with some concerns:

Marian: I don't want Greg using porn—guess I'm old fashioned, but it feels too dirty. I also want to have sex at least twice a week—well, at least we need to be intimate, maybe not intercourse every time.

Greg: Sex twice a week is fine for me, even more is okay. But I do not want to stop using porn.

Marian: Why do you have to continue watching porn when you can now have me? I find this really insulting.

Greg: I don't mean to insult you, and porn is not a substitute for you. Well yes, originally when we didn't have sex I used it to get turned on to masturbate, but now it is just enjoyable.

Marian: Porn is so demeaning to women—how can you continue to watch it?

Greg: I found a special porn site where woman seem to enjoy being exhibitionists. I even found a few videos that turn me on where women dominate men.

Marian: I didn't know you liked that—you mean with whips?

Greg: I didn't know I would get turned on watching men be dominated, but I do.

Marian: I could never compete with that scene. The actresses all have huge tits and skinny bodies. Must admit, I feel jealous of the porn you watch and how it turns you on.

Greg: I'm not asking you to compete. The scene turns me on, not their bodies and I definitely do not want anything like that being done to me. You turn me on without the whips and stuff.

As he said this, he placed his arm around her shoulder and pulled her close. Her face expressed love, and she believe him, so I knew it was time to suggest the agreement.

I recommended they create a simple agreement that took both of their desires into account. They decided that on days they were to have sexplay, Greg would not watch porn. They would have sexplay at least twice a week. If they were to have intercourse, Greg would take his time, use lube, and watch closely for the cues that Marian was ready for penetration.

When the agreement was reached, I encouraged Greg to find ethical pornography* on the Internet. He had not heard of this type of video production, and Marian felt better when I described it involved safe and equitable working conditions along with consent during extreme sexual practice scenes. (A list of ethical pornography sites can be found on the book's website.)

Disclosing feelings about sex and desire can make you vulnerable, especially when it comes to porn and jealousy. So people tend to become secretive and act out. Greg and Marian trusted each other, and they decided to revisit this agreement after one month to see if it was still working comfortably for both of them.

Kim and Michael wanted very much to remain a couple; it was a second marriage for both of them. But Kim's desire to remain in a sexless marriage was becoming impossible for Michael. They had been married for over 20 years, and sex was never an extremely important part of their relationship. They both admitted that it just slowly faded away, and on several occasions when Michael initiated sex, Kim was not interested. Michael initially didn't seem bothered by Kim's lack of desire, because he was busy at work and then had a back injury. But his interest in sex returned when he had more free time and was no longer hurting. That is when the lack of sex became an issue.

They talked about Michael finding a prostitute but he wasn't interested in "doing it" with a person he didn't know. The fear of disease and getting caught by the law were also a major consideration. They were at an impasse, since masturbation wasn't sexually satisfying for Michael, and he wanted intercourse with vaginal penetration. That is when they found me.

After they both filled out the questionnaires found in Chapters 1-4 and Kim had a physical and blood work to make certain there wasn't anything physically amiss with her body, it was decided that they create a contract for a new phase of their marriage.

Kim: Sex was never really a big deal for me. I've had orgasms, but I could never understand all the fuss. Even in my first marriage I wasn't really interested--probably why James cheated and I left him. Couldn't trust him anymore. My ideal agreement would be for me to never have intercourse or be touched intimately. But I really would like to snuggle before we sleep in each other's arms for the night. I like kissing, but no deep kisses.

Michael: (He directed the next statement towards me.) I really would like sex weekly with Kim. I know, that is pie in the sky, but you asked for my ideal.

The one constant: they wanted to remain a couple. Since Michael wanted to remain sexually active and Kim did not, they needed to create an agreement that would allow Kim to be asexual and Michael to get his sexual desires met elsewhere.

> Michael: If I can't have sex with you [Kim] I want to have sex with the same woman on a regular basis. I do not want anonymous one-night stands.

> Kim: I want to meet the woman you are going to have sex with. I guess I have the need to approve. I want to make certain she is not interested in taking you away from me. I don't want you spending the night with her, since that is special. I want that saved only for us.

They agreed Michael could go out with another woman one night a week, and she would be someone Kim approved of before they had sex. They followed up with me quite a few months later. It had taken Michael a while to find the right woman. He finally realized that a number of sexually active older women didn't have many men to choose from and were not interested in taking care of an older man.

That is when his choice of sex partner expanded and he found a lovely widow who was just interested in sex once a week. No strings attached.

I chose these client cases since they cover the points mentioned at the beginning of this chapter:

- You are interested in reviving your sex-life.
>   Or:
- You are interested in being sexual but not as often or using a different style as your partner.
>   Or:
- You have no interest in being sexual but would like to remain in your relationship.

When developing an agreement, keep it simple. Do not get hung up on the "what ifs," but envision the scenarios proposed and what parts of it you want to control. Sometimes that isn't found out until the agreement is "lived out." For couples that see other people intimately, the person at home or with someone else might want to share information about the "other" as part of the agreement. Some couples want to share details while others do not wish to know anything about the other person or time spent with them.

Practical, but important: I suggest adding a clause that the person having sex outside the relationship needs to be tested for STIs* on a regular basis. They also need to make certain that any new sex partner must be tested for STIs. To prevent transmission of STIs, the use of a condom is a must.

Living as a Conscious Couple

You now have the tools to develop and live a *Conscious Coupling* lifestyle. I suggest revisiting your agreements on a regular basis. Together with your partner:

- Reflect on how your "new" relationship is working.
- Resolve any issues.
- Renegotiate your *Conscious Coupling* agreement if necessary.

You might feel that you are venturing into new territory, but according to a large-scale study[2] about 21% of Americans have engaged in CNM. This is a template for expanding a couple's relationship arrangement, whether it is being used to solve disparate marital issues or chosen solely to explore the different styles of relating-ship.*

I leave you with a key phrase—**Be Kind**—to yourself, towards your partner and others. Before you speak your truth please reflect on its impact and **Be Kind.** Especially when negotiating your *Conscious Coupling* agreement and with life in general, this phrase will often produce unexpected positive results. Such a simple yet powerful phrase—**Be Kind.**

Chapter 8: Important Points

- Follow the principle of *Conscious Coupling* to lead your *Authentic Sexual Life*.
- The new monogamy is based on the conscious choices a couple makes regarding their sexual and emotional fidelity.
- Consensual non-monogamy (CNM)* is an umbrella term that refers to various styles couples navigate consensually giving them the option to have one or more outside sexual and/or emotional arrangements.
- *Conscious Coupling* agreement is focused on making certain all parties needs are being met.
- Use the collaborative negotiating style (win/win) to negotiate a non-traditional commitment agreement.
- Revisit your agreement on a regular basis.

TO THE READER

I am most interested in knowing how this book has impacted your relationship with sexuality. I encourage you to go to the book's website and leave a message in the resource section at **http://susanamayer.com/**

I also have an important favor to ask. Whether you read the entire book and filled in all the blank spaces, plan to share the content with your partner, or you just skimmed the chapters and decided it was not what you were expecting, I would appreciate a review. Reviews give potential readers the opportunity to learn about the book from a reader's perspective, and also help authors learn what their readers think. You can leave a review on Amazon whether you bought this book through them or not, as long as you purchased at least one book from them in the past. Or you can leave a review on my website.

Enjoy the process!

— Susana Mayer, PhD

GLOSSARY

***Ageless Sex*:** The physical expression of intimacy taking into consideration emotional needs, aging bodies, health challenges, and one's *Conscious Coupling* lifestyle.

amateur porn: Sexually explicit videos made by real people—that is, not professional actors— taping themselves and putting it online.

andropausal: Relating to andropause or "male menopause." Andropause is not considered a valid concept by all medical practitioners. Proponents claim it is a decline in testosterone levels that can lead to erectile dysfunction and other symptoms similar to those appearing in women's menopause, such as mood-swings, loss of concentration, and depression/malaise. The male drop in hormone levels is gradual and less extreme than for women. Therefore, the male reproductive system does not cease functioning altogether, although after the age of 40 the volume and quality of the sperm decreases, and it can take longer for the partner to conceive. Moreover, these men have a greater chance of fathering children who have genetic abnormalities. Vitamins may improve sperm quality for older men.[1]

arousal (sexual arousal): The involuntary reaction to external stimuli, thoughts, and fantasies.

arousal feedback loop: A cyclical interaction in which sexual partners get turned on by each other's expression of pleasure. This produces a continuous loop of each being turned on by the other person.

asexual: As used in this book: the long-term lack of sexual attraction to other people, or lack of interest in behaving sexually.

atrophic vaginitis: Degeneration and inflammation of the vaginal lining in postmenopausal women, resulting from a decline in estrogen level usually after menopause. The vaginal walls become brittle, thin, inflexible, inflamed, and secrete less fluid, creating symptoms of itching, irritation, and/or pain during vaginal penetration. Also known as vulvovaginal atrophy (VVA).

Authentic Sex Life: An approach to one's own sexuality honoring how one feels about one's sexuality and then consciously acting on it.

collagen: As it pertains to the vagina: a protein fiber that helps strengthen, cushion, and create flexibility in the vaginal wall.

compounded medications: Customized medications with FDA-approved ingredients, formulated by a licensed pharmacist.

Conscious Coupling: As used in this book: the application of the concept *Authentic Sex Life* to the context of a relationship, making certain all people involved in the relationship are having their needs met.

consent: Sexual consent is a voluntary agreement to engage in a specific sexual activity. It is an agreement that may change over time, or even during a single sexplay session. When referring to monogamy and non-monogamy consent, it is an informed contract (often verbal) that each party agrees to follow and which has consequences if violated.

consensual non-monogamy (CNM): an umbrella term that refers to various styles couples navigate consensually, giving them the option to have one or more outside sexual and/or emotional arrangements.

designer relationship: A multitude of relationship styles and arrangements, navigated with consent of all parties involved.

desire discrepancy: A relationship issue in which one partner wants more sex than the other, or wants a different style of sex. Another term in use is *libido discrepancy.*

disorder: (**sexual disorder**): Specific physical or psychological issues that can contribute to a sexual dysfunction, for example, female interest/arousal disorder, female orgasmic disorder, pain disorder. These may affect sexual pleasure.

dungeon: A space with special equipment used for BDSM play.

dysfunction (**sexual dysfunction**): A condition in which the body does not function properly and the results affects the sexual response cycle negatively. Sexual dysfunctions ultimately affect sexual satisfaction.

dyspareunia: A medical term describing all types of painful intercourse, triggered by stimulation or penetration, or simply spontaneous. Pain may occur prior to, during, or after intercourse. This umbrella term includes vaginismus, vulvovaginal atrophy (VVA), vulvodynia, and vestibulitis along with other conditions that produce pain.

edging: Building up to and maintaining a high level of sexual arousal over a long period, before or instead of orgasm/ejaculation.

energy orgasm: When people tune into the ecstasy of intimacy, without physical touch, but not exclusively.

erectile dysfunction (ED): A clinical expression and its abbreviation, now used instead of the term "impotence." ED is the persistent or recurring inability of the penis to become erect or keep an erection long enough for penetration and satisfaction. Frequent "limp penis" can be a sign of a more severe medical condition. Occasional "soft penis" might reflect general stress or issues within a relationship. This would not be considered erectile dysfunction, but erectile dissatisfaction. The term was changed when Viagra was first marketed as a penile enhancing drug (PED).

erotic connection: As used in this book: passionate feelings expressed through verbal and physical forms of affection without sexual stimulation, such as through text messages, hugs, etc. This form of connection focuses on sustaining eroticism between acts of sexual expression.

erotic plasticity: The impact that situational, cultural, and social factors have on an individual's sex drive, which adapts uniquely to all of these for each person.

ethical pornography: Pornography that respects the rights of performers, is created with safe and equitable working conditions, and displays consent in extreme sexual practice scenes.

expanded sex: A collective term that includes the typical genital-focused touching and penetration, as well as any other type of physical expression, including fondling, kissing, stroking, and other forms of intimacy not necessarily confined to the genital area.

extended orgasm: Orgasm in which the physiological orgasm cycle is lengthened.

Human Sexual Response Cycle (HSRC): A model developed by Masters and Johnson to describe the physiological stages of the traditional orgasm.

intimacy: A concept indicating how people relate to each other, especially within a friendship or a romantic/sexual relationship. Conceptually, intimacy involves emotional closeness plus being able to tell one's truth and feel safe. It can include physical closeness.

LGBTQIA: Collective abbreviation for Lesbian, Gay, Bisexual, Transgender, Queer or Questioning, Intersex, and Asexual or Allied communities.

libido: Sexual energy generated by the combination of sex drive and sexual desire. The sex drive is mainly regulated by biology (sex hormones), whereas desire is influenced by psychological and social factors. Sexual arousal can also affect sexual desire.

libido disparity: A relationship issue in which one partner wants more sex than the other, or wants a different style of sex. Another term in use is *desire discrepancy*.

lichen sclerosus (LS): A skin condition with unknown origin. Symptoms include shiny, smooth white spots in the early stages and may progress to the skin's thinning, cracking, and bleeding along with severe itching. Menopausal women are most susceptible, since LS is associated with low estrogen levels. This condition is chronic and progressive, and treatments must continue for the life of the patient. (A list of treatments can be found on the book's website.)

loop (arousal feedback loop): A cyclical interaction in which sexual partners get turned on by each other's expression of pleasure. This produces a continuous loop of each one being turned on by the other person.

menopausal women: In this book, this term refers to any women in any of the stages of menopause:
- Peri-menopause – occurs 10-13 years prior to menopause, usually beginning in a woman's 40s, but can begin as early as her 30s. Average length is 4 years, but may last only a few months or continue as long as 10 years.
- Menopause – occurs when a woman has had no menstrual period for the previous 12 consecutive months. (The average age for women in the United States to begin menopause is 51 years.) Menopause is an event, not a period of time or a state of being.
- Post-menopause – the years after official menopause.

metacommunication: The nonverbal cues (tone of voice, body language, gestures, facial expressions, etc.) that influence how verbal information is interpreted.

monogamish: Characterizing a committed relationship where committed partners agree they can have sex with others under specific conditions set by the couple. The term was coined by sex advice columnist Dan Savage.

multiple orgasms: A sequence of one complete orgasm cycle after another, with an extremely brief refractory period in between.

NAMS: The North American Menopause Society.

neuroplasticity (brain plasticity): The brain's ability to reorganize (compensate) in response to environmental, behavioral, and neural (injury) influences.

nontraditional orgasm: See *orgasm*, but without being genitally focused.

normal: In this book, "normal" describes a vast range of anything to do with sex when sexual consent is given.

open relationship: An agreement between partners allowing each the option to explore emotional and/or sexual relationships with others.

orgasm: As defined by Annie Sprinkle, PhD: "Orgasm is the pleasurable explosion or streaming of built-up erotic or sexual energy in its broadest sense. And it can occur in many different areas of the body, in many different ways."[2]

outercourse: As used in this book: a collective term including any form of sexual activity that does not include penile penetration.

PED: Penile enhancing drugs.

pegging: A sexual activity in which a woman wears a strap-on dildo to perform anal sex on a man.

perineum: The surface area located between the anus and the scrotum or vulva.

Personal Path to Pleasure: An individual's unique method and style of creating pleasure with an ever-changing body.

plasticity (erotic plasticity): The impact that situational, cultural, and social factors have on an individual's sex drive.

polyamory (polyamorous): Consensual romantic relationships with more than one person.

prostate stimulator: A sex toy/aid to self-stimulate the prostate.

pubococcygeus (PC) muscle: A muscle that forms the floor of the pelvic cavity and supports the pelvic organs in both men and women. It is shaped like a hammock and stretches from the pubic bone to the tail bone.

pudendum, pundenda (plural): The external genital organs, most often used for women's genitalia (vulva).

relating-ship: A variant of the noun *relationship* that emphasizes its root in the verb *relate*, recognizing that a relationship is a continually changing arrangement.

rimming (rim job): Slang term for analingus/anilingus. Stimulation of the perineum and anal area with the tongue. This can be performed externally, or internally by using the tongue to penetrate the anus.

sex: Taken from the Merriam-Webster Dictionary:
  Sex (noun)
  : the state of being male or female
  : men or male animals as a group or women or female animals as a group
  : physical activity in which people touch each other's bodies, kiss each other, etc.
  : physical activity that is related to and often includes sexual intercourse
  Sex (verb)
  : to identify the sex of (as in "to sex newborn chicks").
In this book, the word sex (the activity) is to be defined by the reader as whatever makes that person feel that they have had an erotic experience.

sex drive: The innate urge to be sexually satisfied, which is influenced by biological factors and sometimes the state of sexual desire.

sex expanded: A collective term that includes the typical genital-focused touching and penetration as well as any other type of physical expression, including fondling, kissing, stroking, and other forms of intimacy not necessarily confined to the genital area. Synonym of *expanded sex.*

sexologist: A clinical sexologist specializes in human sexual behavior—what people do sexually and how they think and feel about it. These professionals counsel, educate, and offer specific verbal instructions to help clients meet their goals. Clinical sexologists are sex-positive and nonjudgmental when addressing sexual concerns.

sexplay: Enjoyment of sexual pleasure with no goals or expectations involved. This may include all forms of sexual activity, any type of consensual sexual expression. (See *expanded sex, outercourse, sex, sex expanded.*)

sex toys/aids: Objects or gadgets designed to make sex easier and/or enhance sexual pleasure. May be used alone or with a partner(s). Many common objects such as cucumbers and hair clips can be repurposed as sex toys. (See Chapter 6.)

sexual arousal: The physiological reaction to external stimuli, thoughts, and fantasies.

sexual desire: The psychological interest in behaving sexually, influenced by psychological and social factors, and sometimes by the state of sexual arousal.

sexual disorder: Specific physical or psychological issues that can contribute to a sexual dysfunction, for example, female interest/arousal disorder, female orgasmic disorder, pain disorder. These may affect sexual pleasure.

sexual dysfunction: A condition in which the body does not function properly and the results affects the sexual response cycle negatively. Sexual dysfunctions ultimately affect sexual satisfaction.

Sexual Pleasure Model: A concept developed by Susana Mayer, sexologist and author of this book, to describe the basic cycle leading towards sexual pleasure, with and without traditional orgasm.

STI: Sexually transmitted infection.

swinging: Typically, a couple engaging in sexual activities with other people with no emotional attachment or expectations.

traditional orgasm: The physiological pattern of the Human Sexual Response Cycle (HSRC) as described by William Masters and Virginia Johnson. It is a sequence of physical stages that has four phases: arousal, plateau, orgasm and resolution.

urogenital atrophy: Degeneration and inflammation of the vulva, vagina, and lower urinary tract, usually due to low estrogen. Symptoms include: vaginal dryness, irritation and itching, incontinence, urinary urgency, and infections. "Degeneration" refers to a decrease in size or healthiness of a body component.

vagina: The canal connecting the outside of the body to the cervix, which is the opening to the uterus. The elastic, muscular structure of a healthy vaginal canal has a flexible lining that becomes lubricated during physical stimulation. Note that the vagina is a potential space, more like a deflated balloon than a tube. When penetrated, it expands to enclose the penis, dildo, finger, or tampon.

vaginismus: A PC (pubococcygeus) muscle spasm creating a tight constriction that obstructs vaginal penetration. The cause can be of physical or non-physical origin. Some examples of non-physical causes include fears, stress, anxiety, relationship issues, and trauma. Examples of physical causes include medical conditions, soreness and scarring from having given vaginal birth, age-related changes, temporary pelvic pain, pelvic trauma, physical abuse, intense athletic/dance training and injury, and medications.

vasocongestion: Swelling of body tissues with blood. Additional blood flows into the capillaries, which expand and cause the swelling. Sexual stimulation can lead to normal pelvic vasocongestion.

vulva: The external parts of the female genital organs, located in the pubic region. The vulva includes the outer lips, inner lips, clitoris, opening to the urethra, and the opening to the vagina. The internal female genital organs include the vaginal canal, cervix, uterus, fallopian tubes, ovaries, and internal legs (crura) of the clitoris.

vulvodynia: As defined by the International Pelvic Pain Society: "Vulvar pain of at least 3 months duration, without clear identifiable cause, which may have potential associated factors (may be a multifactorial condition)." The two main subtypes are vulvar vestibulitis syndrome and generalized vulvodynia. Vestibulitis is localized to the vestibule, the area at the entry to the vagina. It normally only occurs when provoked by attempted vaginal penetration. Generalized vulvodynia pain can be localized or in multiple areas of the vulva. It can sometime extend to the perineum and inner thighs, often occurring spontaneously and lasting indefinitely. There are more than a dozen different diseases or conditions that can contribute to the symptoms of vulvodynia.

vulvovaginal atrophy (VVA): Degeneration and inflammation of the vaginal lining in postmenopausal women, resulting from a decline in estrogen level usually after menopause. The vaginal walls become brittle, thin, inflexible, inflamed, and secrete less fluid, creating symptoms of itching, irritation, and/or pain during vaginal penetration. Also known as *atrophic vaginitis*

NOTES

Introduction

1. Kilman PR, Norton SP, Boland J, Caid C. Perspectives of sex therapy outcome: a survey of AASECT providers. *Journal of Sex and Marital Therapy.* 1986 Feb;12(2):116-38.

2. I know many of you are probably laughing and thinking I'm delusional, but be aware that this is possible. The oldest verified natural pregnancy occurred when the woman was age 58. To ensure you don't have a late-life baby (unless you are interested in becoming pregnant), you need to stay on birth control until exactly one year from the date your menstruation ceases. Only at that one-year point can you safely stop using birth control.

3. Flibanserin (Addyi) was approved by the FDA in August 2015 to treat *premenopausal* women who suffer from hypoactive (low) sexual desire disorder (HSDD). Colloquially it is referred to as the "pink" Viagra, but this is a misleading comparison. Viagra affects the blood vessels (enhancing a man's erection, for example) and Flibanserin modulates brain chemicals, restoring the balance between inhibition and excitation (restoring desire to prior baseline).

4. Alataş E, Baki Yağci AB. The effect of sildenafil citrate on uterine and clitoral arterial blood flow in postmenopausal women. *Medscape General Medicine.* 2004 Oct 13;6(4):51.

5. MacBride MB, Rhondes DJ, Shuster LT. Vulvovaginal atrophy. *Mayo Clinic Proceedings.* 2010 Jan;85(1):97-94.

6.   Solursh DS, Ernst JL, Lewis RW, et.al. The human sexuality education of physicians in North American medical schools. *International Journal of Impotence Research.* 2003 Oct;15 Suppl 5:S41-5.

7.   Parish SJ. Sexuality education in North American medical schools: current status and future directions. *Journal of Sexual Medicine.* 2013 Jan;10(1):3-17; quiz 18.

8.   Excerpt from Queen C. What sex-positivity is – and is not. https://goodvibesblog.com/sex-positivity-carol-queen-phd/.

9. SAR (Sexual Attitude Reassessment and Restructuring) is a process-oriented seminar designed to examine the participant's attitudes and values related to sexuality. Participants have the opportunity to explore and understand their own perception, beliefs, and attitudes regarding sex and sexuality, which allows them to become more comfortable with the variety of attitudes, behaviors, and practices of their clients. SAR was developed in the late 60s by the National Sex Forum, which evolved into the IASHS in 1974.

10. Trompeter SE, Bettencourt MS, Barrett-Connor E. Sexual activity and satisfaction in healthy community-dwelling older women. *The American Journal of Medicine.* 2012;125(1):37-43.e1.

11. Florence Henderson, 80, says "Sex keeps getting better with age!" *Closer Weekly.* Jan 28, 2015.
http://www.closerweekly.com/posts/florence-henderson-80-says-sex-keeps-getting-better-with-age-50422.

12.   Sexual   satisfaction   in   women   increases   with   age. http://www.elsevier.com/about/press-releases/research-and-journals/sexual-satisfaction-in-women-increases-with-age. Published Jan 3, 2011.

13. Sexual human rights. The Institute for Advanced Study of Human Sexuality.
http://www.humansexualityeducation.com/our-journal.html.

14. Mayer, S, ed. *SenSexual: A Unique Anthology 2013*; Vol 1 & 2 (ebook). Philadelphia, PA: SenSexual Press; 2013.
http://www.amazon.com/SenSexual-Unique-Anthology-2013-Erotica-ebook/dp/B00BA8ZGVY/ref=sr_1_3?

Chapter 1

1. If you recall responding to your partner in a manner you might think of as spiritual, but those experiences have waned, or if you wish to experience this type of sexual pleasure but never have before, then view the resource section on the website for a listing of Gina Ogden's books.

2. "The Evolution of Desire," for the Alexander Foundation for Women's Health: The reference for this interview was based on Dr. Alessandra Graziottin's participation in the Report of the International Consensus Development Conference on Female Sexual Dysfunction: Definitions and Classifications. The Alexander Foundation website is no longer available.

3. Basson R. The female sexual response: a different model. *Journal of Sex & Marital Therapy.* 2000 Jan-Mar;26(1)51-65.

4. Komisaruk BR, Wise N, Frangos E, Liu WC, Allen K, Brody S. Women's clitoris, vagina, and cervix mapped on the sensory cortex: fMRI evidence. *Journal of Sexual Medicine.* 2011 Oct; 8(10):2822-2830.

5. Masters WH, Johnson VE. *Human Sexual Response.* New York, NY: Little, Brown, 1966.

6. Salvatore S, Nappi RE, Parma M, Chionna R, Lagona F, Zerbinati N, Ferrero S, Origoni M, Candiani M, Leone Roberti Maggiore U. Sexual function after fractional microablative CO_2 laser in women with vulvovaginal atrophy. *Climacteric.* 2015 Apr;18(2):219-25.

7. Graham CA, Sanders SA, Milhausen RR, McBride KR. Turning on and turning off: a focus group study of the factors that affect women's sexual arousal. *Archives of Sexual Behavior.* 2004 Dec;33(6):527-538.

8. Kaplan, Helen Singer, and Melvin Horwith. *The Evaluation of Sexual Disorders: Psychological and Medical Aspects.* New York: Brunner/Mazel, 1983.

9. Basson R. The female sexual response: a different model. *Journal of Sex & Marital Therapy.* 2000 Jan-Mar;26(1):51-65.

Chapter 2

1. Kleinplatz PJ, Ménard AD, Pasquet M-P, Paradis N, Campbell M, Zuccarino D, Mehak L. The components of optimal sexuality: a portrait of "great sex." *The Canadian Journal of Human Sexuality.* 2009 18:1-13.

2. Potts A, Grace V, Gavey N, Vares T. "Viagra stories": challenging "erectile dysfunction." *Social Science and Medicine.* 2004 Aug;59(3):489-99.

3. Potts A, Gavey N, Grace VM, Vares T. The downside of Viagra: women's experiences and concerns. *Sociology of Health and Illness.* 2003 Nov;25(7):697-719.

4. Perel, Esther. *Mating in Captivity: Unlocking Erotic Intelligence,* New York, NY: Harper, 2006, pp. 19-37.

5. Northrup, Chrisanna; Schwartz, Pepper; Witte, James. *The Normal Bar: The Surprising Secrets of Happy Couples and What They Reveal About Creating a New Normal in Your Relationship*, Easton, PA: Harmony Press, 2014.

6. Gottman, John. Building a Great Sex Life is Not Rocket Science. The Gottman Institute: A Research-Based Approach to Relationships. https://www.gottman.com/blog/building-great-sex-life-not-rocket-science/.

7. Ibid.

8. Resnick, Stella. *The Heart of Desire: Keys to the Pleasures of Love*, Hoboken, NJ: Wiley, 2012, pp. 109-110.

9. Ibid. pp. 125-130.

10. Nelson, Tammy. *The New Monogamy*. Oakland, CA: New Harbinger, 2012, pp. 125-126.

11. Northrup, Christiane. *The Wisdom of Menopause*. New York, NY: Bantam, 2012, p. 289.

12. Price, Joan. *Naked at Our Age*. Berkeley, CA: Seal, 2011, p. 36.

13. Cornog, M. Sexual body parts: preliminary patterns and implications. *Journal of Sex Research* 1986 22(3):393-398.

14. Rosenblatt, Paul C. *Two in a Bed: The Social System of Couple Bed Sharing*, Albany: State University of New York Press, pp. 84-85.

15. Herbenick, Debby. *Because it Feels Good: A Woman's Guide to Sexual Pleasure and Satisfaction.* Emmaus, PA: Rodale, 2009, p. 23.

16. Mihalko, Reid. Reid About Sex. http://reidaboutsex.com/.

Chapter 3

1. Chivers ML, Seto MC, Blanchard R. The gender and sexual orientation differences in sexual response to sexual activities versus gender of actors in sexual films. *J Pers Soc Psychol.* 2007 Dec;93(6):1108-21.

2. Sinclair Institute. BetterSex Video Series®: Sexplorations. https://www.sinclairinstitute.com/t-about-us.aspx.

3. Dale, Beverly. Rev. Beverly Dale: Reconnecting the Body and Spirit. http://www.beverlydale.org/programs/consulting/.

4. Pertot, Sandra. *Perfectly Normal: Living and Loving with Low Libido.* Emmaus, PA: Rodale, 2005, p. 43.

5. Komisaruk, Barry R., Beyer-Flores, Carlos, Whipple, Beverly. *The Science of Orgasm.* Baltimore, MD: Johns Hopkins University Press, 2006, p. 72.

Chapter 4

1. Fisher, Linda. *Sex, Romance, and Relationships: AARP Survey of Midlife and Older Adults.* AARP, 2010.
https://assets.aarp.org/rgcenter/general/srr_09.pdf

2. Diamond L.M. *Sexual Fluidity: Understanding Women's Love and Desire.* Cambridge, MA: Harvard University Press, 2008, pp. 142-143.

3. Kahr B. *Who's Been Sleeping in Your Head?: The Secret World of Sexual Fantasies.* New York: Basic Books, 2008.

4. Directed Erotic Visualisation© http://esensualwellbeing.com, https://www.patreon.com/bePatron?u=19542337

5. Wise NJ, Frangos E, Komisaruk BR. Activation of sensory cortex by imagined genital stimulation: an fMRI analysis. Socioaffective Neuroscience & Psychology. 2016; 6 Oct 25;6:31481

6. Cross J. Writing Ourselves Whole at the Intersection of Trauma and Desire. http://writingourselveswhole.org/.

7. James E.L. *Fifty Shades of Grey: Book One of the Fifty Shades Trilogy.* New York: Vintage Books, 2012.

8. Sarrel PM, Whitehead MI. Sex and menopause: defining the issues. *Maturitas.* 1985 Sep;7(3):217-24.

9. Herbenick D, Bowling J, Fu T-C, Dodge B, Guerra-Reyes L, Sanders S. Sexual diversity in the United States: results from a nationally representative probability sample of adult women and men. *PLOS ONE.* July 20, 2017. https://journals.plos.org/plosone/article?id=10.1371/journal.pone.0181198

10. Price J. *Naked at Our Age: Talking Out Loud About Senior Sex.* Berkeley, CA: Seal Press, 2011, p. 35.

Chapter 5

1. Defining sexual health: Report of a technical consultation on sexual health, 28-31 January 2002. Geneva, World Health Organization, 2006. http://www.who.int/reproductivehealth/topics/sexual_health/sh_def initions/en/

2. Parish SJ, Nappi RE, Krychman ML, et al. Impact of vulvovaginal health on postmenopausal women: a review of surveys on symptoms of vulvovaginal atrophy. *International Journal of Women's Health.* 2013;5:437-447.

3. Kim HK, Kang SY, Chung YJ, Kim JH, Kim MR. The recent review of the genitourinary syndrome of menopause. *J Menopausal Med.* 2015 Aug;21(2):65-71.

4. Sobecki JN et al. What we don't talk about when we don't talk about sex: results of a national survey of U.S. obstetrician/gynecologists. *The Journal of Sexual Medicine,* 2012 9(5):1285–94.

5. Bois K, Bergeron S, Rosen N, Mayrand MH, Brassard A, Sadikaj G. Intimacy, sexual satisfaction and sexual distress in vulvodynia couples: an observational study. *Health Psychol.* 2016 Jun;35(6):531-40.

6. Panda S, Das A, Santa Singh A, Pala S. Vaginal pH: A marker for menopause. *Journal of Mid-Life Health.* 2014 Jan-Mar;5(1):34-37.

7. Simon JA, Nappi RE, Kingsberg SA, Maamari R, Brown V. Clarifying Vaginal Atrophy's Impact on Sex and Relationships (CLOSER) survey: emotional and physical impact of vaginal discomfort on North American postmenopausal women and their partners. *Menopause.* 2014 Feb;21(2):137-42.

8. Graziottin, Alessandra. Vaginal Biological and Sexual Health—The Unmet Needs.

The paper is based on the lecture presented at the First International Focus Meeting of the Vaginal Erbium Laser Academy in Pisa on March 20th, 2015. Graziottin was Director, Center of Gynecology and Medical Sexology, H. San Raffaele Resnati, Milan, Italy, and President and Founder of the Alessandra Graziottin Foundation for the cure and care of pain in women–NPO.

9. Simon JA, Nappi RE, Kingsberg SA, Maamari R, Brown V. Clarifying Vaginal Atrophy's Impact on Sex and Relationships (CLOSER) survey: emotional and physical impact of vaginal discomfort on North American postmenopausal women and their partners. *Menopause.* 2014 Feb;21(2):137-42.

10. Simon JA, Nappi RE, Kingsberg SA, Maamari R, Brown V. Clarifying Vaginal Atrophy's Impact on Sex and Relationships (CLOSER) survey: emotional and physical impact of vaginal discomfort on North American postmenopausal women and their partners. *Menopause.* 2014 Feb;21(2):137-42.

11. Tinelli A et al. Age-related pelvic floor modifications and prolapse risk factors in postmenopausal women. *Menopause.* 2010 Jan-Feb;17(1):204-12.

12. Nair AN. Dermatosis associated with menopause. *J Midlife Health.* 2014 Oct-Dec; 5(4): 168–75.

13. The International Pelvic Pain Society (IPPS), http://pelvicpain.org/docs/patients/patient-education-brochure.aspx

14. Crandall CJ et al. Breast cancer, endometrial cancer, and cardiovascular events in participants who used vaginal estrogen in the

Women's Health Initiative Observational Study. *Menopause.* 2018 Jan;25(1):11-20.

15. Mac Bride MB, Rhodes DJ, Shuster LT. Vulvovaginal atrophy. *Mayo Clinic Proceedings.* 2010;85(1):87-94.

16. Lindahl SH. Reviewing the options for local estrogen treatment of vaginal atrophy. *Int J Womens Health.* 2014; 6:307–312.

17. Tan O, Bradshaw K, Carr BR. Management of vulvovaginal atrophy-related sexual dysfunction in postmenopausal women: an up-to-date review. *Menopause.* 2012 Jan;19(1):109-17.

18. Whipple B, Komisaruk BR. Elevation of pain threshold by vaginal stimulation in women. *Pain.*1985 Apr;21(4):357-67.

19. Whipple B, Komisaruk, BR. Analgesia produced in women by genital self-stimulation. *The Journal of Sex Research.* 1988 Jan;24(1):130-40.

20. Levin, RJ. The breast/nipple/areola complex and human sexuality. *Sexual & Relationship Therapy,* 2006, May;21(2):237-249.

21. Komisaruk BR, Wise N, Frangos E, Liu W C, Allen K, & Brody S. Women's clitoris, vagina, and cervix mapped on the sensory cortex: fMRI evidence. *Journal of Sexual Medicine.* 2011, Oct;8(10):2822-30.

Chapter 6

1. Klein, Marty, Robbins, Riki. *Let Me Count the Ways: Discovering Great Sex Without Intercourse.* New York: Penguin Putnam Inc., 1998, p 112.

2. Castleman, Michael. "Why So Many Women Don't Have Orgasms. *Psychology Today*, https://www.psychologytoday.com/blog/all-about-sex/201602/why-so-many-women-don-t-have-orgasms.

3. Glickman, Charlie. "Prostate massage." In: *The Ultimate Guide to Sex After 50: How to Maintain—or Regain—a Spicy, Satisfying Sex Life*, by Joan Price. New York: Cleis Press:Start Midnight LLC, 2014, pp. 28-29.

4. Aerts L, Rubin R, Winter A, Goldstein S, Goldstein I. The prevalence of clitoral adhesions in women presenting to the sexual medicine practice. *J Sex Med.* 2017 Apr 14(4): Supplement, e110.

Chapter 7

1. Silverstein RG, Brown ACH, Roth HD, Britton WB. Effects of mindfulness training on body awareness to sexual stimuli: Implications for female sexual dysfunction. *Psychosomatic Medicine.* 2011 Nov-Dec; 73(9):817-825.

2. Brotto LA, Basson R, Group mindfulness-based therapy significantly improves sexual desire in women. *Behavior Research and Therapy.* 2014 Jun;57:43-54.

3. Schlaeger JM, XU N, Mejta CL, Park CG, Wilkie DJ. Acupuncture for the treatment of vulvodynia: a randomized wait-list controlled pilot study. *Journal of Sexual Medicine.* 2015 Apr; 12(4):1019-1027.

4. Khamba B, Aucion M, Lytle M, Vermani M, Maldonado A, Lorio C, Cameron C, Tsirgielis D, D'Ambrosio C, Anand L, Katzman M. Efficacy of acupuncture treatment of sexual dysfunction secondary to antidepressants. *Journal of Alternative and Complementary Medicine.* 2013 Nov;19(11):862-9.

5. Oakley SH, Walther-Liu J, Crisp CC, Paulis RN. Acupuncture in premenopausal women with hypoactive sexual desire disorder: a prospective cohort pilot study. *Journal of Sexual Medicine.* 2016 Sep; 4(3): e176-e181.

6. Dhikav V, Karmarker G, Gupta R, Verma M, Gupta R, Gupta S, Anand K. Yoga in female sexual functions. *Journal of Sexual Medicine.* 2010 Feb; 7(2/2): 964-970.

7. Huang AJ, Rowen TS, Abercrombie P, Subak LL, Schembri M, Plaut T, Chao MT. Development and feasibility of a group-based therapeutic yoga program for women with chronic pelvic pain. *Pain Medicine.* 2017 Oct; 18(10); 1864-1872.

Chapter 8

1. Nelson, Tammy. *The New Monogamy: Redefining Your Relationship After Infidelity.* Oakland, CA: New Harbinger Publications, 2012, p. 25.

2. Haupert ML, Gesselman AN, Moors AC, Fisher HE, Garcia JR. Prevalence of experiences with consensual nonmonogamous relationships: findings from two national samples of single Americans. *J Sex Med.* 2017 Jul 4;43(5):424-440.

Glossary

1. Keskes-Ammar L, Feki-Chakroun N, Rebai T, Sahnoun Z, Ghozzi H, Hammami S, Zghal K, Fki H, Damak J, Bahloul A. Sperm oxidative stress and the effect of an oral vitamin E and selenium supplement on semen quality in infertile men. *Arch Androl.* 2003;Mar-Apr,49(2):83-94.

2. Sprinkle A. *Dr. Sprinkle's Spectacular Sex.* New York, NY: Penguin; 2005, p. 246.

ACKNOWLEDGMENTS

I had no choice but to write this book. My clients, and many of the men and women I interviewed or spoke with informally, confided in me with their intimate stories and insisted I share them with others. This book is my heartfelt "thank you" for trusting me to create composite stories so you would not be outed, and your words would still have the intended impact.

Beyond those personal dialogs, attendees at my Erotic Literary Salon in Philadelphia have shared their experiences since 2008, and participated in the Adult Sex-Ed Q&A sessions. I am grateful for their courage in entrusting the other attendees with the best and worst of their sexual histories. Many of them unknowingly contributed to the composite stories with their own intimate accounts and sexual details.

This book took several years in the making. During the early stages, August Tarrier and Dvora Konstant held my hand while editing the manuscript. Subsequently, I took some time off to work on my own and rethink certain aspects of the text. Then...my present editor seemingly appeared out of nowhere.

If there was ever an angel, her name is Martha Cornog. Retired librarian, an author herself of books and articles, editor, reviewer, and dear friend, she is best known for her *The Big Book of Masturbation*. Martha not only corrected my grammar but was well versed in my topic and caught what I had forgotten, or questioned some of my intent. She made sense out of my dyslexic writing, which was no small task. I am indebted to her for keeping this project alive and well.

Thanks manyfold to my publisher, Jon Drucker at Rhapsody Hill Books, for taking a chance.

Much gratitude to the sexuality researchers and authors who have influenced my work: the late Peggy Brick, Betty Dodson, John Gottman, Debby Herbenick, Marty Klein, Peggy Kleinplatz, Reid Mihalko, Jack Morin, Emily Nagoski, Tammy Nelson, the late Gina Ogden, Esther Perel, Joan Price, Stella Resnick, Tristan Taormino, Beverly Whipple, and Sheri Winston. Along with the other sex-positive professionals I came to know during my graduate studies and extensive networking through the Institute for Advanced Study of Human Sexuality (IASHS) and at conferences of the American Association of Sexuality Educators, Counselors, and Therapists (AASECT). Far too many to list, but you know who you are.

Thank you to the people close to me. Your continued support has made the process of putting words to print possible. A special thank you to my son Sam. His technical expertise often saved the day, but also just knowing he was there for me kept me on my path.

In advance, I thank the readers who are willing to find their authentic sexual voice. You are the reason I have dedicated these past 5+ years to writing this guide.

ABOUT THE AUTHOR

Susana (aka Susan) Mayer, is a board-certified sexologist with the American College of Sexologists (ACS). She holds a doctorate in human sexuality and a master of public health degree. She has retired member status with the American Association of Sexuality Educators, Counselors, and Therapists (AASECT) and the Society for the Scientific Study of Sexuality (SSSS).

She hosts the monthly Erotic Literary Salon/Adult Sex-Ed gatherings that she founded in 2008. They are a verbal sanctuary for sexual expression, to combat sexual shame, and to normalize sex.

Susana resides in Philadelphia, where she is known as the go-to person for information pertaining to sexuality. She is a frequent contributor to NPR radio and various podcasts as well as to online and print publications.

Susana Mayer, PhD, Clinical Sexologist
http://susanamayer.com/
Instagram: susanamayerphd

The Erotic Literary Salon
http://theEroticliterarysalon.com/
Instagram: theeroticliterarysalon

Printed in Great Britain
by Amazon